Conquer Year 6 Maths with CGP!

Ready to test the key facts and methods in Year 6 Maths? Once pupils have got to grips with all the content in our matching Year 6 Maths Knowledge Organiser, they can check how much they've learned with our Knowledge Retriever!

With bonus mixed practice quizzes and a full set of answers too, this book has everything Year 6 pupils need for Maths success!

CGP — still the best! ☺

Our sole aim here at CGP is to produce the highest quality books — carefully written, immaculately presented and dangerously close to being funny.

Then we work our socks off to get them out to you
— at the cheapest possible prices.

Contents

Published by CGP

Editors: Sarah George, Ruth Greenhalgh, Rachel Hickman, Sean McParland, Ali Palin, Sarah Pattison and Dave Ryan.

With thanks to Alison Griffin and Glenn Rogers for the proofreading.

With thanks to Jan Greenway for the copyright research.

ISBN: 978 1 78908 874 8

Printed by Elanders Ltd, Newcastle upon Tyne. Clipart from Corel®

Based on the classic CGP style created by Richard Parson

Text, design, layout and original illustrations © Coordination Group Publications Ltd. (CGP) 2022 All rights reserved.

How to Use This Book

Every page in this book has a matching page in the Year 6 Maths **Knowledge Organiser**. Before filling in the pages in this book, you should have learnt about the topic in your lessons at school and the Knowledge Organiser.

> Read the page and fill in the dotted lines. You might need to write one word, several words, a number or a symbol. Sometimes the first letter of a word is given to help you.

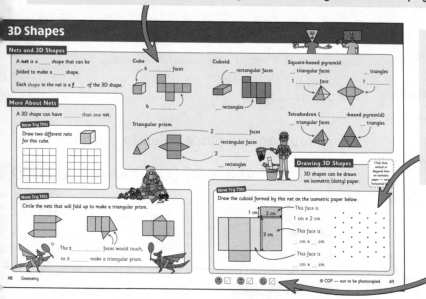

> 'Now Try This' boxes are a chance to have a go at the topic. You may need to draw or complete diagrams, as well as fill in dotted lines.

> Tick the smiley face that shows how happy you feel with the page.

> Once you've finished a page, use the answers at the back of the book to check your work. You might have used a different word to fill in the gap — that's okay, as long as the word has the same meaning.

There are also quizzes throughout the book:

There is a quiz at the end of each section. These quizzes test a mix of content from the previous few pages. There is also a bigger quiz at the end, which covers everything from the book.

Answers to the quizzes are at the back of the book. Write your score in the box at the end of each quiz.

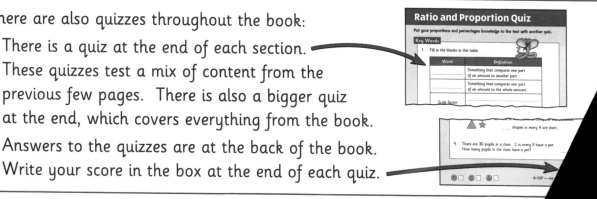

Number Basics

Place Value

ten millions ···

hundreds ···········

52 937 468

···········

··········· ··········· ···········

In words, this number is ················· million, ·····························

and thirty-seven thousand, ·····································.

You can use place value to partition:

52 937 468 = 50 000 000 + 2 000 000

+ ···················· + 30 000

+ ············· + 400 + ······· +

Comparing

The sign ... means less than.

The sign > means

······························.

Now Try This

Use < or > to compare
3 182 034 and 3 270 967.

3 182 034

Both have   1 is smaller

illions.   — than ....

0 967

3 270 967.

Ordering

To put whole numbers in order:

1 Look at the number of ·············· —

numbers with ············ digits are big

2 In numbers with the ············ numbe

of digits, compare the ············ digit:

3 If these are the same, keep moving

right until the digits are **d**···············

ounding

Look at the **decider** — the digit to the .... of the place being rounded to.

Decider less than 5?

Round ....

Decider greater than or equal to 5?

Round ....

To round to the nearest:

ten, look at the .... digit. ⟶

hundred, look at the .... digit. ⟶

thousand, look at the .... digit. ⟶

So 481 537 rounds to:

481 540

....

....

Now Try This

What is 14 526 075 rounded to the nearest ten thousand?

Decider is ...., so round ....

The answer is ....

...cending: from .... to biggest.

.....................: from biggest to smallest.

ow Try This

...ut 2 376 226, 919 423, 1 594 038 and 2 381 702 in descending order.

...his has no millions,

...o it's the ....

...o the order is ...., ..., ..., ...

1 594 038 ⟵ This only has 1 million, so it's smaller than the other two.

2 376 226 ⟵

2 381 702 ⟵ Compare the ten ....

Negative Numbers

Adding and Subtracting

Use **n**............. **l**.......... to add or subtract negative numbers.

To add, start at the negative number and count ....

Now Try This

Work out –9 + 13.

Sketch a number line.

Count on ...... places.

Start at ....

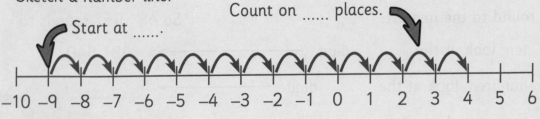

So –9 + 13 = ...

Real-Life Problems

In real-life problems with negative numbers, you'll often have to find the difference between two numbers. A 'change' is just the .... between the numbers at the start and ....

Now Try This

The temperature at midnight was –21 °C. It was –5 °C at noon. the change in temperature.

Count on ... ten and .... ones.

So the change is ...... + ... = ...

3

pied

subtract, count ....

What is –2 – 4?

Start at ....

Count back .... places.

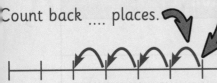

$$-8 \quad -7 \quad -6 \quad -5 \quad -4 \quad -3 \quad -2 \quad -1 \quad 0$$

So –2 – 4 = ...

f you have to cross zero, count the places **to**

nd **after** ...., then .... them together.

$$-5 \quad -4 \quad -3 \quad -2 \quad -1 \quad 0 \quad 1 \quad 2 \quad 3$$

There are .... places from –5 to .... and .... places from .... to 3,

o the difference between –5 and 3 is .... + ... = ...

Finding Differences

To work out differences

between negative numbers:

1 Sketch a ....

2 Count the places ....

the two numbers.

Now Try This

Find the difference
between –36 and –12.

Count on .... tens and .... ones.

$$-36 \qquad\qquad -16 \quad -12$$

The difference is ...... + ... = ...

bank account has –£84 in it.

00 is added. How much is in it now?

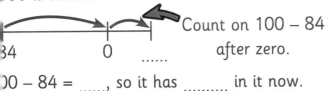

Count on 100 – 84
after zero.

34   0   ......

00 – 84 = ..., so it has .... in it now.

A negative temperature is just

a temperature b........... .... °C.

A .... bank balance means

you **owe money** to the bank.

Place Value Quiz

Get your place value skills in order, because it's time for a quick quiz.

1. Fill in the gaps in this table.

Word	Definition
....	From smallest to biggest.
Descending	....
....	A number less than zero.

3 marks

2. What sign means 'greater than'? ....

1 mark

3. In words, what is the value of the 4 in the number 14 058 377?

   ....

1 mark

4. Which digit is the decider if you're rounding to the nearest hundred? ....

1 mark

5. How should you use a number line to work out −5 + 8?

   ....

   ....

1 mark

6. When Lex rounded their number to the nearest ten thousand, they rounded up. Circle all of the digits below that could have been in the thousands place of Lex's number.

   0   1   2   3   4   5   6   7   8   9   _____

   1 mark

7. Fill in the gaps in the sentences below.

   To compare 7 193 845 and 7 192 916, look at the

   .... digits. 7 193 845 is .... than 7 192 916.   _____

   2 marks

8. How should you work out the difference between a positive number and a negative number?

   ....

   ....   _____

   1 mark

9. Aled writes forty-six million, three hundred and twenty-nine thousand, one hundred and seventy-two as a number.
   What digit is in the hundred thousands place?   ....   _____

   1 mark

10. Fill in the missing numbers and units in these sentences.

    a) It is twelve degrees Celsius below zero.

        The temperature is ....

    b) Kim owes £386 to the bank.

        Kim's bank account has .... in it.   _____

   2 marks

Score: [   ]

Working with Numbers

Common Factors

Factor	A whole number that .... into the number ....
Common factor	A number that is a .... of .... or more numbers.

Now Try This

Find a common factor of 18 and 21.

Factors of 18: ...., 2, ..., 6, ... and 18

Factors of 21: 1, ..., 7 and ......

...... is a common factor of 18 and 21.

Common Multiples

Common multiple:

a number that is a ....

of .... or more numbers.

Now Try This

Find a common multiple of 3 and 4.

Multiples of 3: 3, ..., 9, ..., 15

Multiples of 4: ......, 8, ..., 16

...... is a common multiple of 3 and 4.

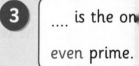

Numbers in coloured squares are the prime numbers up to 100.

Prime Numbers

A prime number has exactly .... **f**.................: ...... and ....

1 1 is NOT a **p**........... **n**............... .

2 All prime numbers end in 1, 3, 7 or 9. .... and .... are the only exceptions.

(But not all numbers ending in 1, 3, 7 or 9 are prime.)

3 .... is the on[...] even prime.

ODMAS

BODMAS tells you the

.... to do things

in a **c**.........................

B — ....   M — ....

O   A — ....

D — ....   S — ....

Now Try This

What is 4 + 10 ÷ 2?

.... first: .... = ...

Then ....:   .... = ...

Now Try This

What is (5 − 1) × 3?

Do the .... first: .... = ...

Then ....: .... = ...

Mental Maths

Partition numbers to make it easier to add or subtract.

Now Try This

What is 7157 + 816?

816 = ... + ... + ...

Add each bit separately:

7157 + ... = 7957

7957 + ... = ...

.... = ...

Work things out in steps.

Now Try This

Aleena has 30 marbles. She loses a fifth of them, then buys 4 more. How many does she have now?

1 Work out one fifth of 30:

30 ÷ .... = ...

2 Subtract from 30:

30 − .... = ...

3 Add 4: .... + 4 = ...

2	3	4	5	6	7	8	9	10
12	13	14	15	16	17	18	19	20
22	23	24	25	26	27	28	29	30
32	33	34	35	36	37	38	39	40
42	43	44	45	46	47	48	49	50
52	53	54	55	56	57	58	59	60
62	63	64	65	66	67	68	69	70
72	73	74	75	76	77	78	79	80
82	83	84	85	86	87	88	89	90
92	93	94	95	96	97	98	99	100

Multiplying and Dividing

Long Multiplication

P.................... the 2-digit number. M.............. each bit separately, then ....

> **Now Try This**
>
> Work out 1571 × 24.
>
> ① Find 1571 × 4.
>
> $$\begin{array}{r} 1\ 5\ 7\ 1 \\ \times\qquad 2\ 4 \\ \hline 6\ 2\ 8\ 4 \\ {}_2\ {}_2 \end{array}$$
>
>
>
> 4 × 70 = ..., so put .... in the
>
> .... column and carry
>
> .... to the .... column.
>
> 4 × 1000 = ..., plus
>
> carried .... is ....
>
> ② Find 1571 × 20.
>
> $$\begin{array}{r} 1\ 5\ 7\ 1 \\ \times\qquad 2\ 4 \\ \hline 6\ 2\ 8\ 4 \\ 3\ 1\ 4\ 2\ 0 \\ {}_1\ {}_1 \end{array}$$
>
> Don't fo
> — it's 2C
> not 2 ×
>
> 20 × 70 = ..., so put .... in
>
> .... column and carr
>
> to the .... column
>
> 20 × 500 = ..., plus
>
> carried .... is ....

Short Division

> **Now Try This**
>
> What is 4133 ÷ 17?
>
> $$17\overline{)4\ 1^{..}3\ 3}$$
>
> 17 × 2 = ..., so
>
> 17 goes into 41 ....
>
> with .... left over.
>
> $$17\overline{)4\ 1^{..}3^{..}3}$$
>
> 17 × 4 = ..., so
>
> 17 goes into 73 ....
>
> times with .... left over.
>
> $$17\overline{)4\ 1^{..}3^{..}3}\ ^{r}$$
>
> 17 × 3 = ..., so
>
> 17 goes into 53 ....
>
> times with .... left over.
>
> So 4133 ÷ 17 = ... remainder ....

Long Division

Now Try This

Work out 2278 ÷ 16.

16 goes into 22 ...., so write ... above 22. 22 – 16 = ...,

so write .... below and move the next digit (7) down.

```
         ... ... ...
16 | 2 2 7 8
   – ... ...
       – ... ...
          – ... ...
             ...
```

16 × 4 = 64, so 16 goes into

67 .... times. Write ....

above the 7. 67 – 64 = ...,

so write .... below and

move the next digit down.

16 × 2 = 32, so 16 goes into 38

.... Write .... above the 8.

38 – 32 = ..., so write .... below.

So 2278 ÷ 16 = ... remainder ....

> There are no more digits to bring down, so this is the remainder.

3 Add together.

```
      1 5 7 1
  ×       2 4
      6 2 8 4   ← ①
  + 3 1 4 2 0   ← ②
  .... .... .... .... ....
         1
```

71 × 24 = 6284 + 31 420

= ....

Remainders

Remainder: the bit .... after a division.

Write a remainder: | as a number | as a fraction | as a decimal |

27 ÷ 5 = ... r ....   27 ÷ 5 = ... $\frac{....}{....}$ 27 ÷ 5 = ...

Now Try This

A tray can hold 8 mugs. How many trays are needed to hold 52 mugs?

52 ÷ 8 = ... remainder ....

.... trays won't be enough, so .... trays will be needed.

Calculation Problems

Wordy Problems

1 Pick out the important information in the question.

2 Turn it into maths.

> ### Now Try This
>
> Romesh has 16 red blocks, 18 yellow blocks and 9 blue blocks. How many blocks does he have in total?
>
> 16 + 18 = ... Then add on the 9: .... + 9 = ...
>
> So he has .... blocks in total.

Estimating

To estimate answers by rounding:

1 Round to easier numbers — e.g. to the nearest

t........ or the nearest w.......... n................ .

2 Work out the calculation using the easier numbers.

> ### Now Try This
>
> Estimate 119 ÷ 9.
>
> Round both numbers
>
> to the nearest ....:
>
> 119 ÷ 9 ≈ .... ÷ ...... = ...

> ### Now Try This
>
> Estimate 10.84 × 6.12.
>
> Round both numbers to
>
> the nearest w.......... n................:
>
> 10.84 × 6.12 ≈ ..... × .... = ...

≈ means " _____ ".

olve problems with more than one calculation
working things out one step at a time.

drink is made from 2000 ml
lemonade and 400 ml of
ange juice. Jenny shares the
ink equally between 12 glasses.
ow many ml is in each glass?

.... ml + ... ml = ... ml

is shared between 12 glasses, so

ork out .... ÷ 12. ...... ÷ 12 = 2,

.... ÷ ...... = ...

there is .... ml in each glass.

Cinema tickets cost £8 for adults
and £4.50 for children. Sally buys
3 adult tickets and 2 child tickets.
How much change does she get
from £40?

3 adult tickets costs .... × £.... = £.......

2 child tickets costs .... × £.......... = £....

Sally spends £...... + £.... = £....... in total,

so she gets £....... – £....... = £.... change.

Checking

E.................... to check answers.

Either find two numbers the answer

lies ...., or round and check that

your answer is .... to the estimate.

Use estimation to check 6.1 × 8.1 = 49.41.

6.1 × 8.1 ≈ .... × .... = ... This is close

to 49.41, so the answer seems sensible.

Use estimation to check
6.74 × 9 = 52.62.

6 × 9 = ... and 7 × 9 = ...

6.74 is between 6 and 7,

so the answer to 6.74 × 9 is

between .... and ....

So this answer is ....

Calculations Quiz

See how much your knowledge has multiplied by having a go at this quick quiz.

1. Fill in the gaps in this table.

Word	Definition
....	A whole number that divides into the number exactly.
Remainder	....
....	A number that has exactly two factors: 1 and itself.
Common multiple	....

4 marks

Now Try These

2. Circle the number below that is a common multiple of 8 and 12.

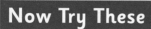 16　　36　　28　　24　　32

1 mark

3. What is the first step when doing a long multiplication?

....

1 mark

4. Give the three different ways of writing a remainder.

1. ....

2. ....

3. ....

5. List the first 5 prime numbers.

............, ..., ..., ... and ....

6. Which part of the calculation 12 − 4 ÷ 2 should you do first: the subtraction or the division?

....

7. Give two ways that you could use estimating to check an answer.

1. ....

2. ....

8. 1, 2 and 4 are common factors of 16 and 24.
What is the other common factor of these two numbers? ....

9. What is the first thing you would do to estimate the answer to 19.7 ÷ 4.3?

....

Score:

Fraction Basics

Equivalent Fractions

Equivalent fractions have different

d.................................., but are ....

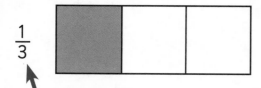

$\frac{1}{3}$

These represent the ....

amount, so they're equivalent.

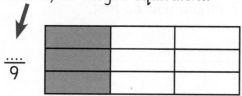

$\frac{....}{9}$

Matching Denominators

To put a group of fractions
over the same denominator:

1 Find a common **m**................

of the ....

2 Turn each fraction into an

.... fraction with

the common .... as

the ....

Simplifying

Simplifying: turning a fraction int▮

an .... fraction with

the .... possible numbers

Divide the top and bottom

by the .... number.

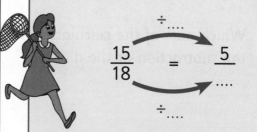

$$\frac{15}{18} = \frac{5}{....}$$

Dividing by the biggest

common **f**............. of the

top and bottom will get you

straight to a simplified fraction.

Give answers to fraction
questions as simplified fractions.

Now Try This

Turn $\frac{3}{4}$ and $\frac{4}{5}$ into equivalent

fractions with the same denominato▮

Multiples of 4: 4, 8, 12, ..., ...

Multiples of 5: 5, 10, 15, ..., ...

Ordering Fractions

If all fractions have the same denominator, compare the **n**........................... Fractions with bigger **n**........................ are ....

For fractions with different denominators:

Write them as equivalent fractions with the same ....

Compare the ....

Now Try This

Which of $\frac{5}{8}$ and $\frac{7}{12}$ is bigger?

Find .... fractions.

$$\frac{5}{8} \overset{\times\,....}{\underset{\times\,....}{=}} \frac{......}{24} \qquad \frac{7}{12} \overset{\times\,....}{\underset{\times\,....}{=}} \frac{......}{24}$$

...... > ......, so $\frac{......}{......}$ is bigger.

Ordering Fractions Bigger Than 1

Turn any mixed numbers into .... fractions.

Then follow the steps for proper fractions above.

Now Try This

Put $\frac{11}{6}$, $\frac{12}{5}$ and $2\frac{4}{15}$ in order from biggest to smallest.

1. Turn the mixed number into an improper fraction.

2. Turn into .... fractions.

$$2\frac{4}{15} = \frac{(2\times......)+4}{15} = \frac{......}{15}$$

$$\frac{11}{6} \overset{\times\,....}{\underset{\times\,....}{=}} \frac{......}{30} \qquad \frac{12}{5} \overset{\times\,....}{\underset{\times\,....}{=}} \frac{......}{30} \qquad \frac{......}{15} \overset{\times\,....}{\underset{\times\,....}{=}} \frac{......}{30}$$

3. Put them in order by comparing numerators. $\frac{......}{30}, \frac{......}{30}, \frac{......}{30}$

4. Write them in their original forms. ...., ..., ...

...se the common multiple ......:

$$\overset{\times\,....}{\underset{\times\,....}{\frown}} \frac{......}{......} \qquad \frac{4}{5} \overset{\times\,....}{\underset{\times\,....}{\frown}} \frac{......}{......}$$

... the answer is $\frac{......}{......}$ and $\frac{......}{......}$.

Fraction Calculations

Adding and Subtracting Fractions

You can only add or subtract fractions with the same ....

Only add or subtract the ....

— leave the .... as they are.

Now Try This

Work out $\dfrac{3}{4} - \dfrac{1}{9}$.

$$\dfrac{3}{4} \xrightarrow{\times\ ....} \dfrac{......}{......}$$

$$\dfrac{1}{9} \xrightarrow{\times\ ....} \dfrac{......}{......}$$

$$\dfrac{......}{......} - \dfrac{......}{......} = \dfrac{......\ -\ ......}{......} = \dfrac{......}{......}$$

Mixed Numbers

To add or subtract mixed numbers:

1 Convert them into

.... fractions.

2 Make sure the ....

fractions have the

.... denominator.

Now Try This

Work out $4\dfrac{2}{3} + 2\dfrac{2}{3}$.

$$4\dfrac{2}{3} = \dfrac{(4 \times ....) + 2}{3} = \dfrac{......}{3}$$

$$2\dfrac{2}{3} = \dfrac{(.... \times ....) + ...}{3} = \dfrac{......}{3}$$

$$\dfrac{......}{3} + \dfrac{......}{3} = \dfrac{......}{3} = ...$$

Give your answer as a mixed number.

Dividing by Whole Numbers

To divide a fraction by a whole number:

$$\dfrac{2}{5} \div 3 = \dfrac{2}{5 ......} = \dfrac{2}{......}$$

M.............. the

....

by the whole number.

Leave th[...]

....

alon[...]

$$\dfrac{2}{5} \ \cdots\ \dfrac{2}{15}$$

The denominator gets bigger,

so the fraction is ....

Multiplying Two Fractions

1 Multiply the

n......................

2 Multiply the

d...........................

3 S................
if needed.

When you multiply two proper fractions, the answer is s............... than either fraction.

$$\frac{1}{3} \times \frac{1}{5} = \frac{1}{15}$$

$$\frac{1}{15} < \frac{1}{3}$$

$$\frac{1}{15} \cdots \frac{1}{5}$$

Now Try This

Work out $\frac{5}{6} \times \frac{2}{3}$.

1   ÷ **3**

$$\frac{5}{6} \times \frac{2}{3} = \frac{5 \times ....}{6 \times ....} = \frac{......}{......} = \frac{......}{......}$$

2   ÷ ....

Give your answer as a s............................. fraction.

D............... by 4 is the same as multiplying by $\frac{1}{4}$.

This is because multiplying and dividing are i...........................

$$\frac{3}{7} \div 4 = \frac{3}{7 \times ....} = \frac{3}{......}$$

$$\frac{3}{7} \times \frac{1}{4} = \frac{3 \times ....}{7 \times ....} = \frac{3}{......}$$

Now Try This

$\frac{3}{8}$ of a bottle of squash is shared equally between 5 people. What fraction of the bottle do they each get?

$$\frac{3}{8} \div .... = \frac{3}{8 \times ....} = \frac{......}{......} \text{ of the bottle}$$

Decimals

Multiplying and Dividing by 10, 100 and 1000

To multiply by: **Shift all of the digits:**

10 ⟹ 1 place to the ....

     O t h   T O t
8.53 × 10 = ...

100 ⟹ .... places to the ....

     O t h   H T O
8.53 × 100 = ...

1000 ⟹ .... places to the ....

     O t h   Th H T O
8.53 × 1000 = ...

Add **z**.......... as placeholders to fill any empty places.

Multiplying Decimals

1. Do a multiplication using **w**.......... numbers.

2. Work out how many times **b**.............. this answer is than the answer to the decimal multiplication.

3. **D**............ to find the answer to the decimal multiplication.

Now Try This

Work out 3.18 × 6.

Find 318 × 6.

    3 1 8
×   6
─────────
....

This is 100 times bigger than 3.18 × 6.

.... ÷ 100 = ...

So 3.18 × 6 = ...

Dividing Decimals

Do a division with **w**.......... numbers.

↓

Work out how much **b**.........

this is than the answer to th~~e~~ decimal division.

↓

D............ to find the answe~~r~~ to the decimal division.

Estimate to check your answer.

divide by 10, shift the

...gits **1 place** to the ....

$29.43 \div 10 = $ ....

divide by 100, shift the

...gits .... **places** to the ....

$1350 \div 100 = 13.50 = $ ....

divide by 1000, shift the

...gits .... **places** to the ....

$41 \div 1000 = $ ....

Remove any unneeded zeros.

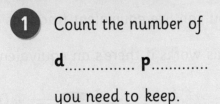

Rounding Decimals

1 Count the number of

d................ p............

you need to keep.

2 Look at the decider (the

next digit to the ....).

3 Round up if the decider

is .... or bigger.

Round down if the

decider is .... or smaller.

Now Try This

Round 6.492 to 2 decimal places.

You need to keep 2 decimal

places, so the decider is the

$6.49|2$

.... digit.

.... is smaller than 5, so round .... to ....

Now Try This

Work out $3.72 \div 4$.

Find $372 \div 4$.

```
        ..............
    4 | 3  7  2
```

So .... $\div 4 = $ ....

.... $\div 100 = $ ....

So $3.72 \div 4 = $ ....

$3.72 \div 4 \approx 4 \div 4 = $ ....

Now Try This

Round 14.97 to 1 decimal place.

$14.9|7$ The decider is bigger than ....,

so round .... to ....

Your answer must have 1 decimal place.

Fractions, Decimals & Percentages

Using Equivalent Fractions

You can use equivalent fractions to write some fractions as decimals.

This works if there's an equivalent with a **d**........................ of 10, 100 or 1000

$$\frac{24}{30} = \frac{....}{10} = 0.....$$ ÷ ....   ÷ .... $\frac{1}{10} = 0....$

$$\frac{7}{25} = \frac{......}{100} = 0.......$$ × ....   × .... $\frac{1}{100} = 0.......$

$$\frac{1}{1000} = 0.........$$

$$\frac{11}{200} = \frac{......}{1000} = 0..........$$ × ....   × ....

Common Conversions

Learn all of these conversions:

$$\frac{1}{4} = 0....... = ...\%$$

$$\frac{....}{4} = 0....... = 75\%$$

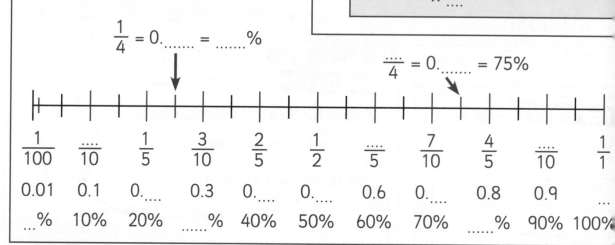

$\frac{1}{100}$	$\frac{....}{10}$	$\frac{1}{5}$	$\frac{3}{10}$	$\frac{2}{5}$	$\frac{1}{2}$	$\frac{....}{5}$	$\frac{7}{10}$	$\frac{4}{5}$	$\frac{....}{10}$	$\frac{1}{1}$
0.01	0.1	0.....	0.3	0.....	0.....	0.6	0.....	0.8	0.9	...
...%	10%	20%	......%	40%	50%	60%	70%	......%	90%	100%

Fractions as Divisions

A fraction is just another way of writing a division.

$$\frac{\text{numerator}}{\text{denominator}} = ... \div ....$$

So $\frac{1}{5} = ... \div .... = 0...$

Work out the division to convert a fraction into a **d**................

Work out the division (**n**........................ ÷ **d**........................).

| Fraction | | Decimal |

Use a denominator of 10 if there's 1 decimal place,

100 if there are 2 and 1000 if there are 3. Put the digits after

the point as the **n**......................... **S**................ if needed.

M................ by .... and add a % sign.

| Decimal | | Percentage |

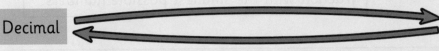

D............ by .... and remove the % sign.

Put it over a denominator of ...., remove the % sign and simplify if needed.

| Percentage | | Fraction |

Find an equivalent fraction with a denominator

of .... and add a ..... sign to the numerator.

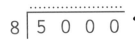

Now Try This

Write $\frac{5}{8}$ as a decimal.

$\frac{5}{8}$ = ... ÷ ....   Work out 5000 ÷ 8 first.

$$8 \overline{| 5 \ 0 \ 0 \ 0}$$

So 5 ÷ 8 = ... ÷ 1000 = ...

Now Try This

What is 0.62 as a fraction?

0.62 has .... decimal places,

so use a denominator of ....

$$\frac{62}{........} \begin{array}{c} \div \ .... \\ = \frac{......}{......} \\ \div \ .... \end{array}$$

Fractions, Decimals & Percentages Quiz

See if you know your fractions from your decimals (and percentages) in this quiz

Key Words

1. Fill in the gaps in this table.

Word	Definition
Equivalent fractions	....
....	Turning a fraction into an equivalent fraction with the smallest possible numbers.

2 marks

Key Diagrams

2. Fill in the missing fractions, decimals and percentages on this number line. Simplify any fractions.

Fraction: ....

Decimal: ....

Percentage: ....

Fraction: ....

Decimal: ....

Percentage: ....

Fraction: ....

Decimal: ....

Percentage: ....

0 ————————————————————————— 1

Fraction: ....

Decimal: ....

Percentage: ....

Fraction: ....

Decimal: ....

Percentage: ....

Fraction: ....

Decimal: ....

Percentage: ....

6 marks

3. To round 3.647 to 1 decimal place,
   do you need to round up or down?   ....

   _____
   1 mark

4. How should you divide a fraction by a whole number?

   ....

   ....
   _____
   1 mark

5. To multiply a number by 1000, how should you shift the digits?

   ....
   _____
   1 mark

6. Rhys has three improper fractions that all have different
   denominators. What should he do first to put them in order?

   ....

   ....
   _____
   1 mark

7. Give two methods you can use to write a fraction as a decimal.

   1. ....

   2. ....
   _____
   2 marks

8. Asha is trying to work out 7.56 ÷ 6. She has found that
   756 ÷ 6 = 126. What does she need to do next?

   ....
   _____
   1 mark

Score: [   ]

Relative Sizes

Scaling

M............... to scale amounts up.

D........... to scale amounts down.

Now Try This

4 pencils cost 44p.

How much will 9 pencils cost?

Scale .... to find the cost

of 1 pencil: .... = ...

Then scale .... to find the cost

of 9 pencils: .... = ...

Ratios

Ratios compare o...... part

to .... part.

○ ○ □ ○ ○ □

There are .... circles and .... squares.

For every 2 circles, there is ....

The **ratio** is " .... to ....

You can write this ratio as ....:.....

Scale Factors

The **scale factor** is the number each

side of a shape is .... by

when it is **e**....................

Now Try This

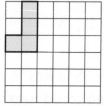

Enlarge this shape by
a scale factor of 2.

Multiply each side length

by the ....

New lengths = ... lengths × ....

Unequal Sharing

Three steps to share things unequal▌

1 Find the .... number of shar▌

2 Work out what .... share is.

3 **M**............... to find the number

of **s**............. you want.

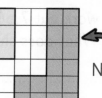

New length = ... × .... = ...

New length = ... × .... = ...

Proportions compare one .... to the ....

.... pieces of fruit in every 5 are apples.

$\frac{...}{5}$ of the pieces of fruit are apples.

... piece of fruit in every 5 is a banana.

$\frac{...}{5}$ of the pieces of fruit are bananas.

ow Try This

bracelet has 2 red beads
r every 7 white beads.
here are 6 red beads.
ow many white beads
e there?

... $\begin{pmatrix} 2 \text{ red to } 7 \text{ white} \\ 6 \text{ red to } ? \text{ white} \end{pmatrix}$ × ....

7 × .... = ... white beads

The ratio of red to white beads is 2:7.

ow Try This

Matt and Jill share £60.
Matt gets £7 for every £3 Jill gets.
How much does Jill get?

here are .... + ... = ... shares in total.

ach share is £.................. = £....

ill gets .... = £......

Matt and Jill share the money in the ratio 7:3.

Now Try This

There are 20 cows in a field.
3 in every 4 cows are brown.
How many of the cows are brown?

There are 20 ÷ 4 = ... lots

of .... cows in the field.

.... cows in each lot are brown,

so .... = ... cows are brown.

KEEP OFF
THE GRASS

find a scale factor,

ivide an e..................

.... by the matching

d l.............

Now Try This

Shape B is an enlargement of shape A.
Find the scale factor of the enlargement.

A
4 cm

(not to scale)

B
12 cm

Base of shape B = ... cm

Base of shape A = ... cm

Scale factor = ... = ...

Using Percentages

Percentages of Amounts

To find 10% of a number, divide it by ....

To find 50% of a number, divide it by ....

To find **20%**, find 10% then .... by ..... .

To find **5%**, find 10% then .... by ..... .

Now Try This

Find 10% of 720.

10% of 720 = ... ÷ ...

= ....

Now Try This

A bag has 15%
off in a sale.
It originally cos
£60. How muc
is the discount?

Numbers as Percentages of Other Numbers

To write a number as a percentage of a total:

1 Put the .... amount as the .... of a fraction.

2 Put the number you're looking for as the ....

3 Convert to a ....

Now Try This

There are 8 green fish and 12 yellow fish in a tank.
What percentage of the fish in the tank are green?

2 .... fish are green.

In total, there are

....

......

.... + ... = ... fish.

3 $\dfrac{....}{....} = \dfrac{.....}{100} = ...$% are green.

×....

×....

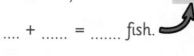
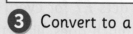

Comparing with Percentages

Now Try This

Find 30% of 80.

0% of 80 = ... ÷ .... = ...

30% of 80 = ... = ...

0% of £60 = £....... ÷ ......

= £....

% of £60 = £.... ÷ .... = £....

o 15% = ... = £....

15% off!

Compare amounts by converting
them into percentages.

Now Try This

Ayo won £25 in a prize draw and spent
£7 of it. Tanya won £10 and spent £2.
Who spent a bigger percentage
of their prize money?

Ayo:

× ....
$$\frac{7}{25} = \frac{.....}{100} = ...\%$$
× ....

Tanya:

× .....
$$\frac{2}{10} = \frac{.....}{100} = ...\%$$
× .....

......% > ......%, so ....

spent a bigger percentage.

Now Try This

Niall has 600 ml of slime. He uses 420 ml in a prank.
Greta has 500 ml of slime. She uses 300 ml to make a slime monster.
Who uses a smaller percentage of their slime?

Niall:
÷ ....
$$\frac{420}{600} = \frac{.....}{100} = ...\%$$
÷ ....

Greta:
÷ ....
$$\frac{300}{500} = \frac{.....}{100} = ...\%$$
÷ ....

......% < ......%, so .... uses a smaller percentage.

Ratio and Proportion Quiz

Put your proportions and percentages knowledge to the test with another quiz.

1. Fill in the blanks in this table.

Word	Definition
....	Something that compares one part of an amount to another part.
....	Something that compares one part of an amount to the whole amount.
Scale factor	....

3 marks

Now Try These

2. What should you divide by to find 50% of an amount? ....

1 mark

3. Marie and Aziz share 24 toys in the ratio 3:5.
    What is the first step to work out how many toys Marie gets?

    ....

1 mark

4. A square with sides of 4 cm is enlarged.
    After the enlargement, the sides are 20 cm long.
    What is the scale factor of the enlargement? ....

1 mark

5. Harry buys 12 notebooks. He spends £36 in total.

   a) How would you work out the cost of 1 notebook?

   ....

   b) How much would 5 notebooks cost?   £ ....

   _____
   2 marks

6. When you're finding 30% of a number, what is the next step after you have found 10%?

   ....

   _____
   1 mark

7. A bag contains 3 blue marbles and 9 red marbles.
   Tim writes a fraction to help him work out what
   percentage of the marbles in the bag are blue.
   What number should go on the denominator?   ....

   _____
   1 mark

8. Look at the shapes below.

   a) What is the ratio of stars to triangles?

   .... : ....

   b) Fill in the blanks to complete this sentence.

   .... shapes in every 4 are stars.

   _____
   2 marks

9. There are 30 pupils in a class. 2 in every 3 have a pet.
   How many pupils in the class have a pet?   ....

   _____
   1 mark

Score: [   ]

Sequences and Formulas

Finding Rules for Sequences

Rule of a sequence: tells you how to get from one **t**......... to the next.

Find the rule by working out the **d**..................... between the ....

Now Try This

The first four terms in a sequence are 1, 4, 7 and 10. What is the rule to get from one term to the next?

1   4   7   10

The rule is " ....

the previous number".

Now Try This

The first four terms in a sequence are 27, 23, 19 and 15. What is the rule to get from one term to the next?

27   23   19   15

The rule is " ....

.... the previous number".

Continuing a Sequence

Use the rule to find more terms in the sequence.

Now Try This

The first four terms in a sequence are 2, 9, 16 and 23. Find the next three terms in the sequence.

2   9   16   23

The rule is " ....

the previous number".

Next three terms:

.... = ...

.... = ...

.... = ...

Writing Formulas

Now Try This

All the cars in a garage have 4 wheels.

Write a formula to work out the total number of wheels of any number of cars in the garage.

Using Formulas

Formula: a .... that connects two or
more **q**.................., so you can work out
one **q**.............. when you know the others.

1 Write out the formula.

2 Write it again, but with **n**..................
in place of the **w**...........

3 Work it out in stages.

ow Try This

ie first four terms in a sequence
e 13, 11, 9 and 7. Find the
xt two terms in the sequence.

ie rule is " ....
.... the previous number".

ext two terms: .... = ...

                 .... = ...

Now Try This

The formula for the cost in £ of a pizza is:
Cost = 5 + number of toppings × 0.5
How much does a pizza with
4 toppings cost?

Cost = 5 + no. of toppings × 0.5

Cost = 5 + ... × 0.5 ←

Cost = 5 + ... = ...

Use BODMAS.

The pizza costs £.....

....

= .... × ....

The thing you're trying
to find goes before '='.

Now Try This

The formula for the area of a triangle is:
$Area = \frac{1}{2} \times base \times height$
What is the area of the triangle below?

$Area = \frac{1}{2} \times base \times height$

$Area = \frac{1}{2} \times .... \times ....$

$Area = \frac{1}{2} \times .... = ... \ cm^2$

5 cm

6 cm

Missing Numbers

Using Symbols for Missing Numbers

Use a symbol to stand for a number in a problem that you need to find.

1 Choose a **s**.............. and write down what it .... for.

2 Write the information in the question using **n**.................. and **s**..................

3 Get the **s**.............. on its own.

Now Try This

Dani multiplies her age by 3. She gets the answer 27. How old is Dani?

◯ = ...

◯ × 3 = 27

Divide both sides by ....:

◯ = 27 ÷ .... = ...

So Dani is .....

Now Try This

Lyle says: "If you double the number of sweets I have, then subtract 7, you get 9." How many sweets does he have?

☐ = ...

9 + 7 is .... the number of sweets Lyle has.

9 + 7 = ..., so 2 × ☐ = ...

Divide both sides by ....:

☐ = ... ÷ .... = ...

So Lyle has .... sweets.

Pairs of Missing Numbers

Some problems have two missing numbers.

Try numbers until you find ones that work.

Now Try This

P × Q = 8. Find two possible pairs of values for P and Q.

P = 1: 1 × .... = 8, so Q = ...

P = 2: 2 × .... = 8, so Q = ...

P = 4 and Q = ... and

P = 8 and Q = ... are also

possible pairs of values.

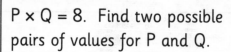

Using Letters for Missing Numbers

You can also use letters to stand for missing numbers.

If you call the missing number x, then:

x + 3 means " .... the number"

x − 1 means " ....

.... the number"

2x means " ....

the number by ...."

$\frac{x}{2}$ means " .... the number by ...."

Now Try This

Roz has 28 stamps. Roz has four times as many stamps as Lin. How many does Lin have?

The number Lin has is unknown.

Call this n stamps.

Then Roz has .... × n stamps.

So ....n = 28

n = 28 ÷ .... = ...

So Lin has .... stamps.

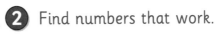

Divide both sides by ......

Sometimes you can simplify the question to make it easier to solve.

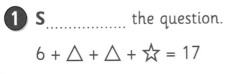

Now Try This

6 + △ + △ + ☆ = 17. Find a possible pair of values for △ and ☆.

1 S................ the question.

6 + △ + △ + ☆ = 17

6 + ...△ + ☆ = 17

....△ + ☆ = ...

So you need values for △ and ☆

that give ....△ + ☆ = ...

2 Find numbers that work.

Try △ = 1:

2△ = 2 × 1 = ...

.... + ☆ = 11, so ☆ = ...

Some other pairs of answers

are △ = 2 and ☆ = ...

and △ = 4 and ☆ = ...

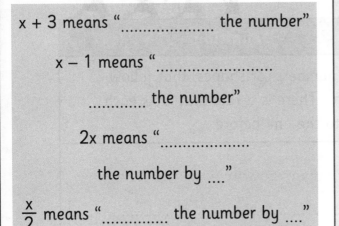

35

Algebra Quiz

Here's the rule for continuing to learn about algebra — have a go at this quiz.

1. Fill in the gaps in this table.

Word	Definition
....	A list of numbers (or shapes) that follow a pattern. There is a rule that links each number to the one before.
Formula	....
....	Each number in a number sequence.

3 marks

Now Try These

2. How do you find the rule for a number sequence?

....

1 mark

3. When you're writing a formula, what goes before the = sign?

....

1 mark

4. Give two things you can use to stand for missing numbers.   .... and ....

1 mark

5. The first four terms in a sequence are 35, 30, 25 and 20.
True or false? The difference between the terms is +5. ....

_____
1 mark

6. Y × Z = 24. Circle the two values below that could be Y and Z.

5   8   7   3

_____
1 mark

7. Ted has C cats. If 5 × C = 35,
what step do you need to do to find C? ....

_____
1 mark

8. The first four terms in a sequence are 3, 9, 15 and 21.
Write down the next three terms.

..............., ... and ....

_____
1 mark

9. The number of points scored in a card game is given
by the formula: Points = 2 × number of cards + 1
Samira has 2 cards. How many points does she have? ....

_____
1 mark

10. Fill in the gaps to simplify this missing number problem.

⃝ + 3 + ▢ + ▢ = 18   ➡   ⃝ + ... ▢ = ...

_____
2 marks

11. A group of friends go to a show. Tickets cost £7.

a) Complete this formula:
Total cost of tickets (in £) = number of friends × ....

b) How much would 6 tickets to the show cost? £...............

_____
2 marks

Score: [   ]

Units

Converting Units

M_____ to go from a big unit to a small unit.

D_____ to go from a small unit to a big unit.

These are the conversion factors:

Length

1 cm	.... mm
.... m	100 cm
1 km	.... m

Mass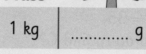

1 kg	.... g

Volume

.... litre	1000 ml

Now Try This

Marco is 120 cm tall.
How tall is he is metres?

.... cm = 1 m

So divide by ....:

.... cm ÷ .... = ... r

Converting Units of Time

You may need to use a few steps to convert units of time.

1 minute	.... seconds
1 hour	.... minutes
1 day	.... hours
1 week	.... days
1 year	.... days

There are
366 days in a
l....... y.........

Now Try This

How many hours are in 2 weeks?

① First convert to days:

1 week = ... days

2 weeks = ... × .... = ... days

② Then convert to hours:

1 day = ... hours

14 days = ... × .... = ... hours

Now Try This

How many seconds are in 4 hours?

First convert to minutes:

1 hour = ... minutes   .... × .... = ... minute

A bottle holds 0.5 litres of water.
How many ml is this?

1 litre = ... ml

So multiply by ....:

.... litres × .... = ... ml

How far is 25 miles in kilometres?

1 First divide by ....:

.... ÷ .... = ...

2 Then multiply by ....:

.... × .... = ... km

Miles and Kilometres

divide by ....

then multiply by ....

8 km ≈ 5 miles

Kilometres

Miles

divide by ....

then multiply by ....

'≈' means

....

....

hen convert to seconds:

minute = ... seconds

.... × .... = ... seconds

How many miles are in 96 km?

1 First divide by ....:

.... ÷ .... = ...

2 Then multiply by ....:

.... × .... = ... miles

Perimeter, Area and Volume

Area and Perimeter

.... is the space inside a 2D shape.

.... is the distance around the outside of a shape.

Area of Triangles

Area of a triangle

$= \dfrac{1}{2} \times$ .... $\times$ ....

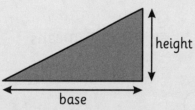

height

base

Now Try This

Find the area of this triangle.

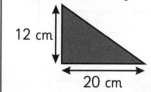

12 cm

20 cm

The base is .... cm.

The height is ...... cm.

Area $= \dfrac{1}{2} \times$ .... $\times$ ...... $=$ .... cm²

Area of Parallelograms

Area of a parallelogram

$=$ base $\times$ ....

height

base

Now Try This

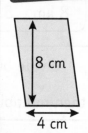

8 cm

4 cm

Find the area of this parallelogram.

Area $=$ base $\times$ ....

Area $=$ .... $\times$ .... $=$ .... cm²

Now Try This

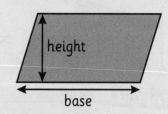

6 cm

9 cm

Find the area of the grey part of this parallelogram.

Area of parallelogram $=$ .... $\times$ .... $=$ .... cm²

Area of coloured triangle $= \dfrac{1}{2} \times$ .... $\times$ .... $=$ .... cm²

Area of grey part $=$ .... $-$ .... $=$ .... cm²

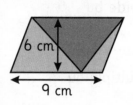

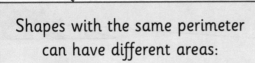

Shapes with the same perimeter can have different areas:

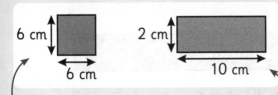

6 cm | 6 cm

2 cm | 10 cm

Perimeter = ... + ... + ... + ... = ... cm

Area = ... × .... = ... cm²

Perimeter = ... + ... + ... + ...

= .... cm

Area = ... × .... = ... cm²

Shapes with the same area can have different perimeters:

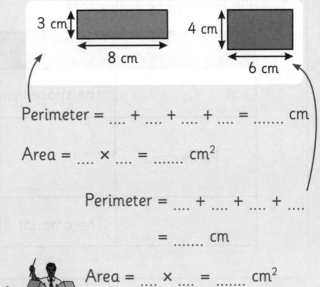

3 cm | 8 cm

4 cm | 6 cm

Perimeter = ... + ... + ... + ... = ... cm

Area = ... × .... = ... cm²

Perimeter = ... + ... + ... + ...

= .... cm

Area = ... × .... = ... cm²

Volume of Cubes and Cuboids

Volume: ....

Volume of a cuboid = ... × .... × ....

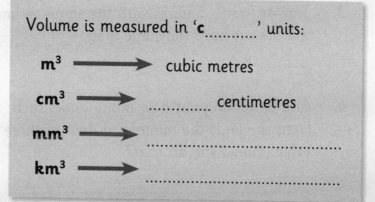

height | length | width

Now Try This

Calculate the volume of this cuboid.

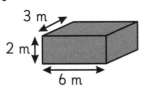

3 m

2 m

6 m

Volume = ... × .... × ....

Volume = ... m³

Volume is measured in 'c.........' units:

m³ ⟶ cubic metres

cm³ ⟶ .... centimetres

mm³ ⟶ ....

km³ ⟶ ....

Measurement Quiz

Convert your knowledge into answers by having a go at this quick quiz.

1. Fill in the gaps in this table.

Word	Definition
....	The space inside a 2D shape.
Perimeter	....
....	The amount of space a 3D shape takes up.

3 marks

Now Try These

2. If you want to convert from a big unit to a small unit, should you multiply or divide?

   ....

   1 mark

3. True or false? Shapes with the same perimeter will always have the same area.

   ....

   1 mark

4. Arla is working out how many hours there are in three weeks. First, she finds the number of days in three weeks. What should she do next?

   ....

   1 mark

5. How many seconds are in 3 minutes?

....

6. How would you use the conversion 8 km ≈ 5 miles to convert a distance in kilometres to miles?

....

7. Fill in the blanks in the formula below.

Area of a triangle = ... × .... × ....

8. Fill in the blanks to complete these unit conversions.

a) 1 km = ... m

b) 2 cm = ... mm

c) 500 g = ... kg

9. What is the area of the parallelogram on the right?

.... cm^2

5 cm

7 cm

10. What is the formula to work out the volume of a cuboid?

....

Score:

2D Shapes

Quadrilaterals

A **quadrilateral** is a shape with .... sides.

Rhombus

Square	Rectangle	

Square

.... equal sides

4 equal angles of ....°

.... pairs of parallel sides

4 lines of symmetry

Rectangle

.... pairs of equal sides

4 equal angles of ....°

2 pairs of **p**............... sides

.... lines of symmetry

Rhombus

.... equal sides

.... pairs of equal angles

.... pairs of parallel sides

2 lines of **s**....................

Other Polygons

Equilateral triangle

.... equal sides

3 equal angles of ....°

No parallel sides

.... lines of symmetry

Isosceles triangle

.... equal sides

.... equal angles

No **p**............... sides

1 .... of symmetry

Regular polygon: a shape with all

equal .... and equal ....

Irregular polygon: a shape

that doesn't have all equal

s........... and **e**........ **a**...............

Circles

...............: distance from

the **e**........ to the centre

diameter: distance across the

circle through the **c**...............

...................................:

the outside edge of a circle

Now Try This

Draw an equilateral triangle with sides of 3 cm.

Equilateral triangles have

.... equal sides

and three ....° angles.

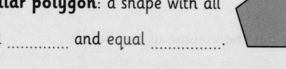

ite

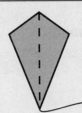

Parallelogram

Trapezium

.... pairs of equal sides

.... pairs of equal sides

1 pair of **p**.............. sides

.... pair of equal ....

2 pairs of equal ....

...... parallel sides

2 pairs of **p**.............. sides

line of **s**.......................

.... lines of symmetry

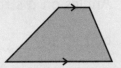

Most trapeziums have ....
lines of symmetry, but ones
like this have exactly ....:

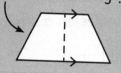

The diameter is

.... the radius.

Now Try This

The diameter of a circle
is 14 cm. What is the
radius of the circle?

Diameter = ... × radius

Radius = diameter ÷ ....

Radius = ... ÷ ....

= ....

Drawing Polygons

1 Measure and draw sides
with a ....

2 Measure and draw angles
with a ....

Then draw the final line
to complete the triangle.

Draw the
first side.

Mark the 60° angle
with a dot.

Draw a 3 cm line
through the dot.

Angles

Angle Rules

1 Angles on a straight line
add up to ....°.

$a + b + c =$ .... °

2 Angles around a point
add up to ....°.

$w + x + y + z =$ .... °

Now Try This

What is the size of angle p?

Angles on a straight line add up to ....°.

So $56° + 71° + p =$ .... °

$p =$ ....° $- 56° - 71° =$ .... °

Now Try This

What is the size of angle q?

Angles around a point add up to ....°.

So $128° + 64° +$ ....° $+ q =$ .... °

$q =$ ....° $- 128° - 64° -$ ....° $=$ .... °

3 Vertically opposite angles are ....

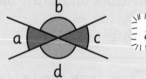

$a =$ ...... and $b =$ ......

Angles in a Triangle

Angles in a triangle add up to ....°.

Now Try This

What is the size of angle r?

r and the 54° angle are

v.................. o..................,

so they are e.......... . So r = ...°.

Now Try This

What is the size of angle x in this triangle?

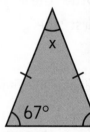

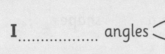

Angles in a Quadrilateral

Angles in a quadrilateral

add up to .... °.

What is the size of angle s
in this quadrilateral?

Angles in a quadrilateral

add up to .... °, so

s + 54° + 57° + 108° = ... °

s = ... ° – 54° – 57° – 108°

= .... °

The triangle is isosceles,

so this angle is .... °.

Angles in a triangle add up to .... °,

so x + 67° + ... ° = ... °.

x = ... ° – .... ° – .... ° = ... °

Angles in Polygons

E.................... angles

I.................... angles

For all polygons:

Interior angle = ... ° – exterior angle

Sum of exterior angles = ... °

Sum of interior angles = (n – ....) × .... °

> n is the
> number
> of sides.

For regular polygons ONLY:

1 All interior angles are e..........

2 All exterior angles are e..........

3 Exterior angle = $\dfrac{..........°}{n}$

Find the exterior and interior
angles in a regular hexagon.

A hexagon has .... sides,

so n = ...

Exterior angle = $\dfrac{..........°}{n}$

= $\dfrac{..........°}{..........}$ = ...°

Interior angle = ... ° – .... °

= .... °

3D Shapes

Nets and 3D Shapes

A **net** is a .... shape that can be

folded to make a .... shape.

Each shape in the net is a **f**......... of the 3D shape.

Cube

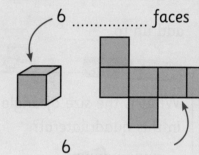

6 .... faces

6 ....

More About Nets

A 3D shape can have .... than one net.

Now Try This

Draw two different nets for this cube.

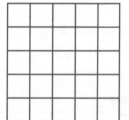

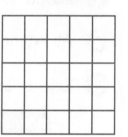

Triangular prism

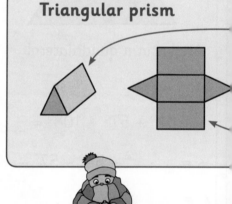

Now Try This

Circle the nets that will fold up to make a triangular prism.

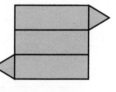

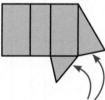

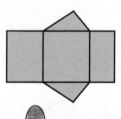

The **t**.................. faces would touch,

so it .... make a triangular prism.

Cuboid

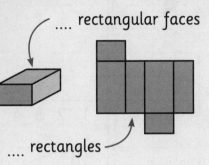

.... rectangular faces

.... rectangles

2 .... faces

.... rectangular faces

2 ....

.... rectangles

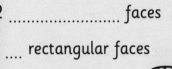

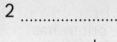

Square-based pyramid

.... triangular faces

1 .... face

.... triangles

1 ....

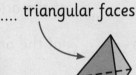

Tetrahedron (................. -based pyramid)

.... triangular faces

.... triangles

Drawing 3D Shapes

3D shapes can be drawn on isometric (dotty) paper.

Now Try This

Draw the cuboid formed by this net on the isometric paper below.

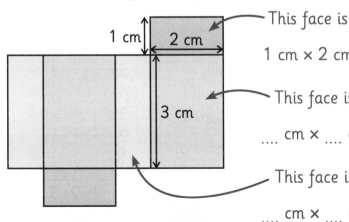

1 cm   2 cm

3 cm

This face is
1 cm × 2 cm

This face is
.... cm × .... cm

This face is
.... cm × .... cm

Coordinates & Transformations

Coordinates

Each quarter of the grid is called a **q**.....................

Coordinates tell you the position of a point.

number on the .... axis

$\searrow$ (x, y) $\nwarrow$

       number on the .... axis

If x is positive, the point is .... of the origin.

If x is negative, the point is .... of the origin.

If y is positive, the point is .... the origin.

If y is negative, the point is .... the origin.

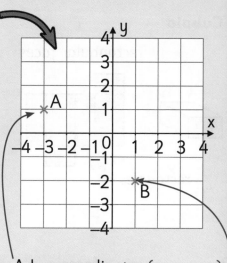

A has coordinates (......, ...).

B has coordinates (......, ...).

The origin has coordinates (...., ...).

Translations

Translation: when a shape slides from one place to another.

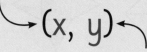 woof

 meow

Translating by a

positive number moves

shapes right or ....

Translating by a

negative number moves

shapes .... or down.

Now Try This

Translate shape A 2 units horizontally and −4 units vertically. Label the new shape B.

Find the coordinates of the translated vertex Z on shape B.

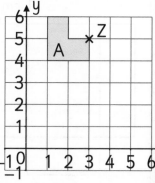

Missing Coordinates

Use shape facts to find missing coordinates.

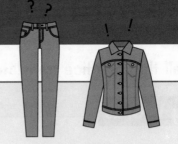

Now Try This

The shape on the right is a square.
What are the coordinates of point A?

A is directly .... B, so they have the ....

x-coordinate. So the x-coordinate of A is ......

The **d**........................ between the x-coordinates of B and C is ......,

so each side of the square is ...... units. A is ...... units below B,

so the y-coordinate of A is ...... – ...... = ... So A has coordinates (......, ...).

(−1, 3) B ×   × C (3, 3)

A ×   × D

Reflections

Reflect shapes in a **m**............ **l**.........

Each point and its reflection are the **s**.......... distance from the ....

① Count the number of units to the **m**............ **l**.........

② Count the **s**.......... number on the other side of the **m**............ **l**.........

③ Draw the **r**....................... point.

mirror line

Draw the reflection of the shape above.

Vertex A is 3 units .... the x-axis, so the
reflected vertex A is 3 units .... the x-axis.

Translate the shape 2 units to the ....
and 4 units ....

The coordinates of the translated vertex Z are (......, ...).

Geometry Quiz

Will all that practice translate to success? Find out with this quick quiz...

Key Words

1. Fill in the gaps in the table below.

Word	Definition
Quadrilateral	....
Irregular polygon	....
....	When a shape slides from one place to another on a grid.
....	A 2D shape that can be folded to make a 3D shape.

4 marks

Key Diagrams

2. Fill in the gaps to label the parts of a circle.

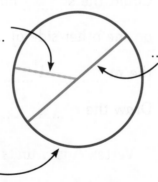

....

....

....

3 marks

3. Look at the shape on the right.

   a) What is the name of the shape? ....

   b) How many lines of symmetry does it have? ....

   _____
   2 marks

4. Give the values of angles c and d.

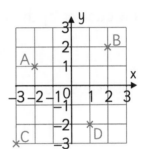

   c = ...°   d = ...°

   _____
   2 marks

5. What is the sum of the
   angles in a quadrilateral? ....°

   _____
   1 mark

6. Which point on the grid on the right
   (A-D) has a positive y-coordinate
   and a negative x-coordinate? ....

   _____
   1 mark

7. Complete the table with the properties for each shape.

Shape	Pairs of equal angles	Pairs of parallel sides	Lines of symmetry
Rhombus	2	....	....
Kite	....	....	1
Parallelogram	....	....	....

   _____
   3 marks

8. How do you find the size of an exterior angle on a regular polygon?

   ....

   _____
   1 mark

Score: [ ]

Pie Charts

Pie Chart Basics

Pie charts: show things as **p**........................

A slice of a pie chart is called a **s**..............

A bigger .... means a bigger

p......................

This pie chart shows the favourite sports chosen by 24 pupils in a Year 6 class.

This is a quarter of the pie chart, so a .... of the class chose football.

One .... of 24 is ....

[Pie chart showing: Football, Tennis, Netball, Hockey]

Angles In a Pie Chart

There are ....° in a circl

| Total of the angles in a pie chart = ...° |

This is half of the pie chart, so ....

the class chose tenni

.... of 24 is .....

Drawing Pie Charts

Use a multiplier to work out the .... of each angle.

1 Add up the numbers to find the **t**..........

2 Divide 360° by the .... to find the multiplier.

3 Multiply each number by the .... to get the angle.

Now Try This

The table on the right shows the number of different coloured balls in a bag.
Draw a pie chart to show this information

1 Total = 28 + 51 + 17 + 24 = ...

2 Multiplier = ... ÷ .... = ...

3 Red = 28 × .... = ...°

Blue = 51 × .... = ...°

Green = 17 × .... = ...°

Yellow = 24 × .... = ...°

A survey asked people to vote for their favourite vegetable.
This pie chart shows the results. What is the angle for "turnip"?

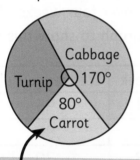

Total of the angles = ... °, so 170° + 80° + ? = ... °.

.... ° − .... ° − .... ° = ... °

So the angle for "turnip" = ... °

80° is the **s**.................. sector,

so "carrot" got the **f**.............. votes.

170° is the **b**.............. sector,

o "cabbage" got the **m**........ votes.

Interpreting Pie Charts

Turn angles into numbers
by finding a fraction or
percentage of the pie chart.

This pie chart shows
how 60 pupils travelled
to school. How many
pupils walked?

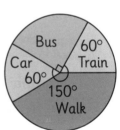

The 'walk' sector is .... °.

Whole chart = ... °,

so the fraction is $\dfrac{..........}{..........} = \dfrac{5}{12}$.

Divide the top and
bottom by 30.

$\dfrac{......}{......} \times 60 = ...$ pupils walked.

Colour	Red	Blue	Green	Yellow
Number	28	51	17	24

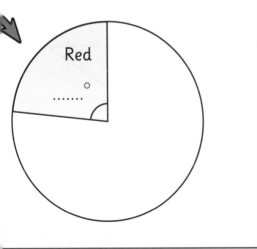

Working with Data

Line Graphs

Line graphs: show how something **c**..................

To plot points on a line graph:

1 Read up from the **h**..................... axis

and across from the **v**............... axis.

2 Draw a point where

the two lines **m**..........

3 Repeat for each point, then

.... them up with straight lines.

Now Try This

The table below shows the number of ice creams sold at a shop over four weeks. Draw a line graph to show this data.

Week	Ice creams sold
1	95
2	85
3	30
4	75

Conversion Graphs

Use conversion graphs to .... between different **u**..........

Put one .... on the horizontal axis and one .... on the vertical axis.

Now Try This

The graph on the right converts between miles and kilometres.

What is 10 miles in kilometres?

Read up from the horizontal axis:

10 miles = ... km

What is 24 kilometres in miles?

Read across from the vertical axis:

24 km = ... miles

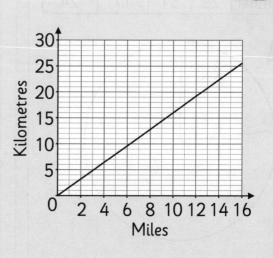

56   Statistics

" .... "

is on the vertical axis.

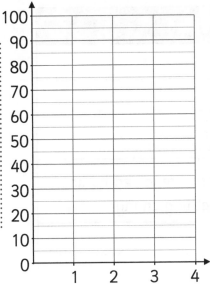

....

The ....

are on the horizontal axis.

This line graph shows the temperature in a garden on one day. How much warmer was it at 2 pm than at 11 am?

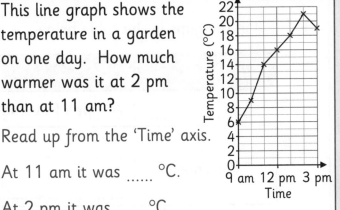

Read up from the 'Time' axis.

At 11 am it was ...... °C.

At 2 pm it was ...... °C.

So it was ...... – ...... = ... °C warmer.

The Mean

The mean is sometimes called 'the

a................'. To find the mean:

1 .... all of the numbers.

2 .... the total by how many numbers there are.

Now Try This

Find the mean of these numbers:

5, 6, 11, 7, 4, 9

5 + 6 + 11 + 7 + 4 + 9 = ...

There are ...... numbers.

.... ÷ .... = ...

So the mean is ....

Now Try This

The weights of some bags of birdseed were 47 g, 53 g, 55 g and 45 g. What was the mean weight?

47 + 53 + 55 + 45 = ...

There are ...... numbers. .... ÷ ...... = ...

So the mean weight was ...... g.

Statistics Quiz

Mmmm pies... Oh sorry, I got distracted... Here, have a go at this lovely quiz.

Key Words

1. Fill in the gaps in the table below.

Word	Definition
....	A type of average.
Pie Chart	....
....	A graph with points that are joined by lines, which shows how something changes.
Conversion Graph	....

4 marks

Now Try These

2. A survey asked people to vote for their favourite dog breed. This pie chart shows the results.

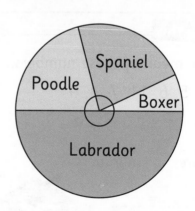

a) Which breed got the fewest votes?

....

b) Which breed got half of the votes?

....

2 marks

3. The table on the right shows the number of ducks that Mona saw in her pond on three different days.

Day	Number of ducks
1	15
2	22
3	9

a) Mona wants to make a line graph to show the data in the table. What data should go on the x-axis?

....

b) Describe how she should plot each point on the graph.

....

....

....

c) Mona also wants to know the mean number of ducks she saw. She adds up the number of ducks. What should she do next?

....

3 marks

4. You can use a multiplier to work out the size of an angle when drawing a pie chart. How do you find the multiplier?

....

....

1 mark

5. This graph shows the height of a plant over four weeks. How much taller was the plant at week 7 than it was at week 3?

....

1 mark

Score:

End of Year Quiz

Sharpen your favourite pencil — here's one more quiz to show what you know.

1. Fill in the gaps in this table.

Word	Definition
Factor	....
....	When a shape slides from one place to another on a grid.
Prime number	....
....	A circular chart that shows things as proportions.
....	The amount of space a 3D shape takes up.
Quadrilateral	....
Remainder	....
....	Fractions that have different denominators, but are equal.
Scale factor	....

9 marks

2. Draw lines to match each word to its definition.

Descending

Something that compares one part of an amount to another part.

Ratio

From smallest to biggest.

Ascending

Something that compares one part of an amount to the whole amount.

Proportion

From biggest to smallest.

3 marks

3. Use the words in this box to complete the definitions below.

| sequence | net | 3D |
| 2D | mean | term | average |

..................: a kind of .... found by adding up all the values then dividing by the total number of values.

..................: a .... shape that can be folded to make a .... shape.

..................: a list of numbers (or shapes) that follow a pattern. There is a rule that links each .... to the one before.

7 marks

4. Patrick wants to round 816 457 to the nearest thousand.

   a) Circle the digit below that he should use as the decider.

   8   1   6   4   5   7

   b) Should he round up or down? ....

   2 marks

5. What number should you multiply by to convert
   a distance in metres into centimetres? ....

   1 mark

6. What is the first step in working out $6 \times (7 + 1)$?

   ....

   1 mark

7. Fill in the blanks with the equivalent decimals,
   percentages or fractions (in their simplest form).

   a) $\dfrac{1}{4}$ = ... %

   b) $0.8 = \dfrac{\text{.......}}{\text{.......}}$

   c) $23\% = 0.$...........

   3 marks

8. How could you use a number line to work out
   the difference between -11 and 16?

   ....

   ....

   1 mark

9. True or false? The radius of a circle is twice
   as long as the diameter.

   ....

   1 mark

10. What two calculations could you do to find two numbers that the answer to 5.27 × 8 lies between?

1. .... 2. ....

2 marks

11. To divide a number by 100, how should you shift the digits?

....

1 mark

12. The sides of a cuboid are measured in m.
What units would you use for the volume of the cuboid?   ....

1 mark

13. The first four terms of a sequence are 21, 17, 13 and 9.

a)   What is the rule for this sequence?

....

b)   What are the next two terms in the sequence?

.... and ....

2 marks

14. Circle the fraction below that is **not** equivalent to $\frac{1}{4}$.

$$\frac{25}{100} \qquad \frac{3}{12} \qquad \frac{10}{40} \qquad \frac{4}{20} \qquad \frac{2}{8}$$

1 mark

15. Rhea is packing 42 books into boxes. Each box holds 8 books. How many books will be left over once she has filled as many boxes as she can?   ....

1 mark

16. What is the sum of the angles on a straight line?   ....°

1 mark

17. Fill in the blanks to complete the sentences below.

The net of a cube is made of .... squares.

The net of a triangular prism is made of

two .... and three ....

3 marks

18. How do you multiply a fraction by another fraction?

....

....

1 mark

19. Greg wants to find the mean of 5, 8, 11, 7 and 4.
What is the first thing he should do?

....

1 mark

20. Look at the shape on the right.

a) What is the size of angle a?

.... °

b) What formula would you use to
work out the area of this shape?

....

2 marks

21. A shape is translated −3 units horizontally and 5 units vertically.
Complete the sentence below.

The shape is translated 3 squares to the ....

and 5 squares ....

2 marks

22. What is the first step in putting $\frac{3}{5}$, $\frac{5}{8}$ and $\frac{7}{10}$ in order from smallest to biggest?

....

....

23. There are 4 shirts for every jumper in a drawer. There are 2 jumpers. How many shirts are there?

....

24. What two steps would you do to work out 5% of a number?

1. ....

2. ....

25. Hannah has 5 more toy cars than Jakub.
If x = the number of toy cars Jakub has, how would you write the number of toy cars Hannah has? ....

26. 40 people were asked their favourite pets.
The results are shown on a pie chart.

a) 8 people said 'cats'. What is the first thing you would do to find the angle of the 'cats' sector on the pie chart?

....

b) The sector for 'dogs' is one quarter of the pie chart. How many people said 'dogs'? ....

Score:

Answers

Place Value

Pages 2-3 —
Number Basics

Place Value

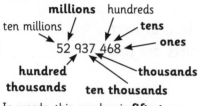

In words, this number is **fifty-two** million, **nine hundred** and thirty-seven thousand, **four hundred and sixty-eight**.

52 937 468 = 50 000 000 + 2 000 000 + **900 000** + 30 000 + **7000** + 400 + **60** + 8

Rounding

Look at the decider — the digit to the **right** of the place being rounded to.

Decider less than 5? Round **down**.

Decider greater than or equal to 5? Round **up**.

...ten, look at the **ones** digit.

...hundred, look at the **tens** digit.

...thousand, look at the **hundreds** digit.

So 481 537 rounds to: 481 540, **481 500, 482 000**

Decider is **6**, so round **up**.

The answer is **14 530 000**.

Comparing

The sign < means less than.

The sign > means **greater than**.

Both have **3** millions.

1 is smaller than **2**.

So 3 182 034 < 3 270 967.

Ordering

1. Look at the number of **digits** — numbers with **more** digits are bigger.

2. In numbers with the **same** number of digits, compare the **first** digits.

3. If these are the same, keep moving right until the digits are **different**.

Ascending: from **smallest** to biggest.

Descending: from biggest to smallest.

This has no millions, so it's the **smallest**.

Compare the ten **thousands**.

So the order is **2 381 702, 2 376 226, 1 594 038, 919 423**.

Pages 4-5 —
Negative Numbers

Adding and Subtracting

Use **number lines** to add or subtract negative numbers.

To add, start at the negative number and count **on**.

Start at **–9**. Count on **13** places.

So –9 + 13 = **4**.

To subtract, count **back**.

Start at **–2**. Count back **4** places.

So –2 – 4 = **–6**.

Finding Differences

1. Sketch a **number line**.

2. Count the places **between** the two numbers.

Count on **2** tens and **4** ones.

The difference is **20 + 4 = 24**.

If you have to cross zero, count the places to and after **zero**, then **add** them together.

There are **5** places from –5 to **0** and **3** places from **0** to 3, so the difference between –5 and 3 is **5 + 3 = 8**.

Real-Life Problems

A 'change' is just the **difference** between the numbers at the start and **end**.

Count on **1** ten and **6** ones.

So the change is **10 + 6 = 16 °C**.

Number line: **16**

100 – 84 = **16**, so it has **£16** in it now.

A negative temperature is just a temperature **below 0** °C.

A **negative** bank balance means you owe money to the bank.

Pages 6-7 —
Place Value Quiz

Key Words

1. **Ascending**: From smallest to biggest.
   Descending: **From biggest to smallest.**
   Negative number: A number less than zero.
   (1 mark for each)

Now Try These

2. > (1 mark)

3. Four million (1 mark)

4. Tens (1 mark)

5. E.g. Start at –5 and count on 8 places. (1 mark)

6. The thousands digit was the decider, so it must have been greater than or equal to 5. So 5, 6, 7, 8 and 9 should be circled.
   (1 mark for all five circled)

Answers

7. To compare 7 193 845 and 7 192 916, look at the **thousands** digits. 7 193 845 is **greater** than 7 192 916. (1 mark for each)

8. Starting at the negative number, count the places to and after zero, then add them together. (1 mark)

9. The number is 46 329 172, so **3** is in the hundred thousands place. (1 mark)

10. a) The temperature is **−12 °C**.
    b) Kim's bank account has **−£386** in it. (1 mark for each)

Calculations

Pages 8-9 —
Working with Numbers

Common Factors

Factor: A whole number that **divides** into the number **exactly**.

Common factor: A number that is a **factor** of **two** or more numbers.

Factors of 18: **1**, 2, **3**, 6, **9** and 18
Factors of 21: 1, **3**, 7 and **21**
3 (or **1**) is a common factor of 18 and 21.

Common Multiples

Common multiple: a number that is a **multiple** of **two** or more numbers.

Multiples of 3: 3, **6**, 9, **12**, 15
Multiples of 4: **4**, 8, **12**, 16
12 is a common multiple of 3 and 4.

BODMAS

BODMAS tells you the **order** to do things in a **calculation**.

B — **Brackets**
O
D — **Division**
M — **Multiplication**
A — **Addition**
S — **Subtraction**

Divide first: **10 ÷ 2 = 5**
Then **add**: **4 + 5 = 9**

Do the **brackets** first: **5 − 1 = 4**
Then **multiply**: **4 × 3 = 12**

Prime Numbers

A prime number has exactly **two factors**: **1** and **itself**.

1. **1** is NOT a **prime number**.

2. All prime numbers end in 1, 3, 7 or 9. **2** and **5** are the only exceptions.

3. **2** is the only even prime.

Mental Maths

816 = **800 + 10 + 6**
7157 + **800** = 7957
7957 + **10** = **7967**
7967 + 6 = 7973

30 ÷ 5 = **6**
Subtract from 30: 30 − **6** = 24
Add 4: **24** + 4 = **28**

Pages 10-11 —
Multiplying and Dividing

Long Multiplication

Partition the 2-digit number. **Multiply** each bit separately, then **add**.

4 × 70 = **280**, so put **8** in the **tens** column and carry **2** to the **hundreds** column.

4 × 1000 = **4000**, plus carried **2000** is **6000**.

20 × 70 = **1400**, so put **4** in the **hundreds** column and carry **1** to the **thousands** column.

20 × 500 = **10 000**, plus carried **1000** is **11 000**.

```
      1 5 7 1
    ×     2 4
    ─────────
      6 2 8 4
  + 3 1 4 2 0
    ─────────
    3 7 7 0 4
        1
```

1571 × 24 = 6284 + 31 420
          = **37 704**

Short Division

```
          2
    ┌──────────
  17│ 4 1 ⁷3 3
```
17 × 2 = **34**, so 17 goes into 41 **twice** with **7** left over.

```
        2 4
    ┌──────────
  17│ 4 1 ⁷3 ⁵3
```
17 × 4 = **68**, so 17 goes into 73 **four** times with **5** left over.

```
        2 4 3 r 2
    ┌──────────────
  17│ 4 1 ⁷3 ⁵3
```
17 × 3 = **51**, so 17 goes into 53 **three** times with **2** left over.

So 4133 ÷ 17 = **243** remainder **2**.

Long Division

```
          1 4 2
  16│ 2 2 7 8
    − 1 6
      ─────
        6 7
      − 6 4
        ─────
          3 8
        − 3 2
          ─────
            6
```

16 goes into 22 **once**, so write **1** above 22. 22 − 16 = **6**, so write **6** below and move the next digit (7) down.

16 × 4 = 64, so 16 goes into 67 **four** times. Write **4** above the 7. 67 − 64 = **3**, so write **3** below and move the next digit down.

Answers

$16 \times 2 = 32$, so 16 goes into 38 **twice**. Write **2** above the 8. $38 - 32 = 6$, so write **6** below.

So $2278 \div 16 = 142$ remainder **6**.

Remainders

Remainder: the bit **left over** after a division.

$27 \div 5 = 5$ r **2**

$27 \div 5 = 5\frac{2}{5}$

$27 \div 5 = 5.4$

$52 \div 8 = 6$ remainder **4**

6 trays won't be enough, so **7** trays will be needed.

Pages 12-13 — Calculation Problems

Wordy Problems

$16 + 18 = 34$. Then add on the 9: $34 + 9 = 43$.
So he has **43** blocks in total.

2000 ml + **400** ml = **2400** ml
It is shared between 12 glasses, so work out **2400** ÷ 12. $24 \div 12 = 2$, so **2400** ÷ 12 = **200**.
So there is **200** ml in each glass.

3 adult tickets costs $3 \times £8 = £24$.
2 child tickets costs $2 \times £4.50 = £9$.
Sally spends £24 + £9 = **£33** in total, so she gets £40 – £33 = **£7** change.

Estimating

1. Round to easier numbers — e.g. to the nearest **ten** or the nearest **whole number**.

Round both numbers to the nearest **ten**: $119 \div 9 \approx 120 \div 10 = 12$

Round both numbers to the nearest **whole number**: $10.84 \times 6.12 \approx 11 \times 6 = 66$

≈ means "**approximately equal to**".

Checking

Estimate to check answers. Either find two numbers the answer lies **between**, or round and check that your answer is **close** to the estimate.

$6.1 \times 8.1 \approx 6 \times 8 = 48$

$6 \times 9 = 54$ and $7 \times 9 = 63$
6.74 is between 6 and 7, so the answer to 6.74×9 is between **54** and **63**.
So this answer is **wrong**.

Pages — 14-15 Calculations Quiz

Key Words

1. **Factor**: A whole number that divides into the number exactly.
   Remainder: **The bit left over after a division**.
   Prime number: A number that has exactly two factors — 1 and itself.
   Common multiple: **A number that is a multiple of two or more numbers**.
   (1 mark for each)

Now Try These

2. 16 36 28 (24) 32 (1 mark)

3. Write out the numbers with place value columns aligned. (1 mark)

4. 1. As a number
   2. As a fraction
   3. As a decimal
   (1 mark for each)

5. 2, 3, 5, 7 and 11
   (2 marks for all five correct, otherwise 1 mark for at least three correct)

6. Division (1 mark)

7. 1. Finding two numbers that the answer lies between.

2. Rounding and checking that your answer is close to the estimate.
   (1 mark for each)

8. 8 (1 mark)

9. Round to easier numbers (e.g. to the nearest whole number). (1 mark)

Fractions, Decimals & Percentages

Pages 16-17 — Fraction Basics

Equivalent Fractions

Equivalent fractions have different **denominators** but are **equal**.

These represent the **same** amount, so they're equivalent.

Fraction by diagram: $\frac{3}{9}$

Simplifying

Simplifying: turning a fraction into an **equivalent** fraction with the **smallest** possible numbers.

Divide the top and bottom by the **same** number.

$$\overset{\div 3}{\underset{\div 3}{\frac{15}{18}}} = \frac{5}{6}$$

Dividing by the biggest common **factor** of the top and bottom will get you straight to a simplified fraction.

Matching Denominators

1. Find a common **multiple** of the **denominators**.

2. Turn each fraction into an **equivalent** fraction with the common **multiple** as the **denominator**.

Answers

Multiples of 4: 4, 8, 12, **16**, **20**...

Multiples of 5: 5, 10, 15, **20**, 25...

Use the common multiple **20**.

$$\overset{\times 5}{\underset{\times 5}{\frac{3}{4}}} = \frac{15}{20} \qquad \overset{\times 4}{\underset{\times 4}{\frac{4}{5}}} = \frac{16}{20}$$

So the answer is $\frac{15}{20}$ and $\frac{16}{20}$.

Ordering Fractions

If all fractions have the same denominator, compare the **numerators**. Fractions with bigger **numerators** are **bigger**.

Write them as equivalent fractions with the same **denominator**.

Compare the **numerators**.

Find **equivalent** fractions.

$$\overset{\times 3}{\underset{\times 3}{\frac{5}{8}}} = \frac{15}{24} \qquad \overset{\times 2}{\underset{\times 2}{\frac{7}{12}}} = \frac{14}{24}$$

15 > 14, so $\frac{5}{8}$ is bigger.

Ordering Fractions Bigger Than 1

Turn any mixed numbers into **improper** fractions.

1. $2\frac{4}{15} = \frac{(2 \times 15) + 4}{15} = \frac{34}{15}$

2. Turn into **equivalent** fractions.

$$\overset{\times 5}{\underset{\times 5}{\frac{11}{6}}} = \frac{55}{30} \quad \overset{\times 6}{\underset{\times 6}{\frac{12}{5}}} = \frac{72}{30} \quad \overset{\times 2}{\underset{\times 2}{\frac{34}{15}}} = \frac{68}{30}$$

3. $\frac{72}{30}, \frac{68}{30}, \frac{55}{30}$

4. $\frac{12}{5}, 2\frac{4}{15}, \frac{11}{6}$

Pages 18-19 — Fraction Calculations

Adding and Subtracting Fractions

You can only add or subtract fractions with the same **denominator**.

Only add or subtract the **numerators** — leave the **denominators** as they are.

$$\overset{\times 9}{\underset{\times 9}{\frac{3}{4}}} = \frac{27}{36} \qquad \overset{\times 4}{\underset{\times 4}{\frac{1}{9}}} = \frac{4}{36}$$

$$\frac{27}{36} - \frac{4}{36} = \frac{27 - 4}{36} = \frac{23}{36}$$

Mixed Numbers

1. Convert them into **improper** fractions.

2. Make sure the **improper** fractions have the **same** denominator.

$$4\frac{2}{3} = \frac{(4 \times 3) + 2}{3} = \frac{14}{3}$$

$$2\frac{2}{3} = \frac{(2 \times 3) + 2}{3} = \frac{8}{3}$$

$$\frac{14}{3} + \frac{8}{3} = \frac{22}{3} = 7\frac{1}{3}$$

Multiplying Two Fractions

1. Multiply the **numerators**.

2. Multiply the **denominators**.

3. **Simplify** if needed.

$$\frac{5}{6} \times \frac{2}{3} = \frac{5 \times 2}{6 \times 3} = \overset{\div 2}{\underset{\div 2}{\frac{10}{18}}} = \frac{5}{9}$$

Give your answer as a **simplified** fraction.

When you multiply two proper fractions, the answer is **smaller** than either fraction.

$$\frac{1}{15} < \frac{1}{5}$$

Dividing by Whole Numbers

$$\frac{2}{5} \div 3 = \frac{2}{5 \times 3} = \frac{2}{15}$$

Multiply the **denominator** by the whole number.

Leave the **numerator** alone.

$$\frac{2}{5} > \frac{2}{15}$$

The denominator gets bigger, so the fraction is **smaller**.

$$\frac{3}{8} \div 5 = \frac{3}{8 \times 5} = \frac{3}{40} \text{ of the bottle.}$$

Dividing by 4 is the same as multiplying by $\frac{1}{4}$.

This is because multiplying and dividing are **inverses**.

$$\frac{3}{7} \div 4 = \frac{3}{7 \times 4} = \frac{3}{28}$$

$$\frac{3}{7} \times \frac{1}{4} = \frac{3 \times 1}{7 \times 4} = \frac{3}{28}$$

Pages 20-21 — Decimals

Multiplying and Dividing by 10, 100 and 1000

10 — 1 place to the **left**

100 — **2** places to the **left**

1000 — **3** places to the **left**

8.53 × 10 = **85.3**

8.53 × 100 = **853**

8.53 × 1000 = **8530**

Add **zeros** as placeholders to fill any empty spaces.

To divide by 10, shift the digits 1 place to the **right**.

29.43 ÷ 10 = **2.943**

To divide by 100, shift the digits **2** places to the **right**.

1350 ÷ 100 = 13.50 = **13.5**

To divide by 1000, shift the digits **3** places to the **right**.

41 ÷ 1000 = **0.041**

Multiplying Decimals

1. Do a multiplication with **whole** numbers.
2. Work out how many times **bigger** this answer is than the answer to the decimal multiplication.
3. **Divide** to find the answer to the decimal multiplication.

```
   3 1 8
 ×     6
 1 9 0 8
   1 4
```

$1908 ÷ 100 = \textbf{19.08}$

So $3.18 × 6 = \textbf{19.08}$

Dividing Decimals

Do a division using **whole** numbers.

Work out how many times **bigger** this is than the answer to the decimal division.

Divide to find the answer to the decimal division.

```
     9 3
 4 | 3 7 ¹2
```

So $372 ÷ 4 = \textbf{93}$

$93 ÷ 100 = \textbf{0.93}$

So $3.72 ÷ 4 = \textbf{0.93}$

$3.72 ÷ 4 ≈ 4 ÷ 4 = \textbf{1}$

Rounding Decimals

1. Count the number of **decimal places** you need to keep.
2. Look at the decider (the next digit to the **right**).
3. Round up if the decider is **5** or bigger. Round down if the decider is **4** or smaller.

You need to keep 2 decimal places, so the decider is the **thousandths** digit.

2 is smaller than 5, so round **down** to **6.49**.

The decider is bigger than **5**, so round **up** to **15.0**.

Pages 22-23 — Fractions, Decimals & Percentages

Using Equivalent Fractions

This works if there's an equivalent with a **denominator** of 10, 100 or 1000.

$$\overset{÷3}{\frac{24}{30}} = \frac{8}{10} = \textbf{0.8} \qquad \frac{1}{10} = \textbf{0.1}$$
÷3

$$\overset{×4}{\frac{7}{25}} = \frac{28}{100} = \textbf{0.28} \qquad \frac{1}{100} = \textbf{0.01}$$
×4

$$\overset{×5}{\frac{11}{200}} = \frac{55}{1000} = \textbf{0.055}$$
×5

$$\frac{1}{1000} = \textbf{0.001}$$

Common Conversions

$\frac{1}{100} = 0.01 = \textbf{1\%}$

$\frac{1}{10} = 0.1 = \textbf{10\%}$

$\frac{1}{5} = \textbf{0.2} = \textbf{20\%}$

$\frac{1}{4} = \textbf{0.25} = \textbf{25\%}$

$\frac{3}{10} = 0.3 = \textbf{30\%}$

$\frac{2}{5} = \textbf{0.4} = 40\%$

$\frac{1}{2} = \textbf{0.5} = 50\%$

$\frac{3}{5} = 0.6 = 60\%$

$\frac{7}{10} = \textbf{0.7} = 70\%$

$\frac{3}{4} = \textbf{0.75} = 75\%$

$\frac{4}{5} = 0.8 = \textbf{80\%}$

$\frac{9}{10} = 0.9 = 90\%$

$\frac{1}{1} = 1 = 100\%$

Fractions as Divisions

$$\frac{numerator}{denominator} = \textbf{numerator} ÷ \textbf{denominator}$$

So $\frac{1}{5} = \textbf{1} ÷ \textbf{5} = 0.2$

Work out the division to convert a fraction into a **decimal**.

$\frac{5}{8} = 5 ÷ 8$

```
       6 2 5
 8 | 5 0 ²0 ⁴0
```

So $5 ÷ 8 = \textbf{625} ÷ 1000 = \textbf{0.625}$

Converting Between Fractions, Decimals and Percentages

Work out the division (**numerator ÷ denominator**)

Use a denominator of 10 if there's 1 decimal place, 100 if there are 2 and 1000 if there are 3. Put the digits after the point as the **numerator**. **Simplify** if needed.

Multiply by **100** and add a % sign.

Divide by **100** and remove the % sign.

Put it over a denominator of **100**, remove the % sign and simplify if needed.

Find an equivalent fraction with a denominator of **100** and add a **%** sign to the numerator.

0.62 has **2** decimal places, so use a denominator of **100**.

$$\overset{÷2}{\frac{62}{100}} = \frac{31}{50}$$
÷2

Answers

Pages 24-25 — Fractions, Decimals & Percentages Quiz

Key Words

1. Equivalent fractions:
   Fractions that have different denominators, but are equal.
   Simplifying: Turning a fraction into an equivalent fraction with the smallest possible numbers.
   (1 mark for each)

2. Top row: $\frac{1}{10} = 0.1 = 10\%$

   $\frac{3}{5} = 0.6 = 60\%$

   $\frac{3}{4} = 0.75 = 75\%$

   Bottom row: $\frac{1}{5} = 0.2 = 20\%$

   $\frac{1}{2} = 0.5 = 50\%$

   $\frac{9}{10} = 0.9 = 90\%$

   (1 mark for each set of three correct)

Now Try These

3. Down (1 mark)

4. Multiply the denominator by the whole number. (1 mark)

5. Shift all of the digits 3 places to the left. (1 mark)

6. Write them as equivalent fractions with the same denominator. (1 mark)

7. 1. Divide the numerator by the denominator.
   2. Find an equivalent with a denominator of 10, 100 or 1000.
   (1 mark for each)

8. Divide 126 by 100. (1 mark)

Ratio and Proportion

Pages 26-27 — Relative Sizes

Scaling

Multiply to scale amounts up.
Divide to scale amounts down.

Scale **down** to find the cost of 1 pencil: **44p ÷ 4 = 11p**
Then scale **up** to find the cost of 9 pencils: **11p × 9 = 99p**

Ratios

Ratios compare **one** part to **another** part.
There are **4** circles and **2** squares. For every 2 circles, there is **1 square**.
The ratio is "**2 circles** to **1 square**". You can write this ratio as **2 : 1**.

$\times 3 \left(\begin{array}{l} 2 \text{ red to 7 white} \\ 6 \text{ red to ? white} \end{array} \right) \times 3$

7 × 3 = 21 white beads

Proportions

Proportions compare one **part** to the **whole**.

4 pieces of fruit in every **5** are apples.
$\frac{4}{5}$ of the pieces of fruit are apples.

1 piece of fruit in every **5** is a banana.
$\frac{1}{5}$ of the pieces of fruit are bananas.

There are 20 ÷ 4 = **5** lots of **4** cows in the field. **3** cows in each lot are brown, so **3 × 5 = 15** cows are brown.

Unequal Sharing

1 Find the **total** number of shares.
2 Work out what **one** share is.
3 **Multiply** to find the number of **shares** you want.

There are **7 + 3 = 10** shares in total.
Each share is **£60 ÷ 10 = £6**
Jill gets **3 × £6 = £18**.

Scale Factors

The scale factor is the number each side of a shape is **multiplied** by when it is **enlarged**.

Multiply each side length by the **scale factor**.

New lengths = **old** lengths × **2**
New length = **3 × 2 = 6**
New length = **2 × 2 = 4**

To find a scale factor, divide an **enlarged length** by the matching old **length**.

Base of shape B = **12** cm
Base of shape A = **4** cm
Scale factor = **12 ÷ 4 = 3**

Pages 28-29 — Using Percentages

Percentages of Amounts

To find 10% of a number, divide it by **10**.
To find 50% of a number, divide it by **2**.

To find 20%, find 10% then **multiply** by **2**.
To find 5%, find 10% then **divide** by **2**.

10% of 720 = **720 ÷ 10 = 72**

10% of 80 = **80 ÷ 10 = 8**
30% of 80 = **8 × 3 = 24**

10% of £60 = **£60 ÷ 10 = £6**

5% of £60 = **£6 ÷ 2 = £3**

So 15% = **£6 + £3 = £9**

Numbers as Percentages of Other Numbers

1. Put the **total** amount as the **denominator** of a fraction.

2. Put the number you're given as the **numerator**.

3. Convert to a **percentage**.

8 fish are green.
In total, there are **8 + 12 = 20** fish.

$\frac{8}{20}$

$\frac{8}{20} = \frac{40}{100} = \mathbf{40}\%$ are green.

(×5)

Comparing with Percentages

× 4
$\frac{7}{25} = \frac{28}{100} = \mathbf{28}\%$
× 4

× 10
$\frac{2}{10} = \frac{20}{100} = \mathbf{20}\%$
× 10

28% > 20%, so **Ayo** spent a bigger percentage.

÷ 6
$\frac{420}{600} = \frac{70}{100} = \mathbf{70}\%$
÷ 6

÷ 5
$\frac{300}{500} = \frac{60}{100} = \mathbf{60}\%$
÷ 5

60% < 70%, so **Greta** uses a smaller percentage.

Pages 30-31 —
Ratio and Proportion Quiz

Key Words

1. **Ratio**: Something that compares one part of an amount to another part.

Proportion: Something that compares one part of an amount to the whole amount.
Scale factor: **The number each side is multiplied by in an enlargement.**
(1 mark for each)

Now Try These

2. **2** (1 mark)

3. Find the total number of shares (by adding 3 and 5). (1 mark)

4. 20 cm ÷ 4 cm = 5, so the scale factor of the enlargement is 5. (1 mark)

5. a) Divide £36 by 12. (1 mark)
   b) 1 notebook costs £36 ÷ 12 = £3. 5 notebooks cost 5 × £3 = £15. (1 mark)

6. Multiply the 10% value by 3. (1 mark)

7. 3 + 9 = 12 (1 mark)

8. a) **3 : 1** or **6 : 2** (1 mark)
   b) **3** shapes in every 4 are stars. (1 mark)

9. There are 30 ÷ 3 = 10 lots of 3 in the class. 2 pupils in each lot have a pet, so 2 × 10 = 20 pupils have a pet. (1 mark)

Algebra

Pages 32-33 —
Sequences and Formulas

Finding Rules for Sequences

Rule of a sequence: tells you how to get from one **term** to the next.

Find the rule by working out the **difference** between the **terms**.

+3   +3   +3
1   4   7   10

The rule is "**add 3 to** the previous number".

-4   -4   -4
27   23   19   15

The rule is "**take away 4 from** the previous number".

Continuing a Sequence

+7   +7   +7
2   9   16   23

The rule is "**add 7 to** the previous number".
Next three terms:
23 + 7 = 30
30 + 7 = 37
37 + 7 = 44

The rule is "**take away 2 from** the previous number".
Next two terms:
7 – 2 = 5
5 – 2 = 3

Using Formulas

Formula: a **rule** that connects two or more **quantities**, so you can work out one **quantity** when you know the others.

2. Write it again, but with **numbers** in place of the **words**.

Cost = 5 + **4** × 0.5
Cost = 5 + **2** = **7**
The pizza costs £**7**.

Area = $\frac{1}{2}$ × **6** × 5

Area = $\frac{1}{2}$ × **30** = **15** cm^2

Writing Formulas

Total number of wheels = number of cars × 4

Pages 34-35 —
Missing Numbers

Using Symbols for
Missing Numbers

1. Choose a **symbol** and write down what it **stands** for.

Answers

2. Write the information in the question using **numbers** and **symbols**.

3. Get the **symbol** on its own.

$\bigcirc$ = Dani's age

$\bigcirc \times 3 = 27$

Divide both sides by **3**:

$\bigcirc = 27 \div 3 = 9$

So Dani is **9**.

$\square$ = **number of sweets**

9 + 7 is **double** the number of sweets Lyle has.

9 + 7 = **16** so $2 \times \square = 16$.

Divide both sides by **2**:

$\square = 16 \div 2 = 8$

So Lyle has **8** sweets.

Using Letters for Missing Numbers

x + 3 means "**add 3 to** the number"

x − 1 means "**subtract 1 from** the number"

2x means "**multiply** the number by **2**"

$\frac{x}{2}$ means "**divide** the number by **2**"

Then Roz has **4 × n** stamps.

So **4n = 28**

Divide both sides by **4**.

n = 28 ÷ **4** = **7**

So Lin has **7** stamps.

Pairs of Missing Numbers

P = 1: 1 × **8** = 8, so Q = **8**.

P = 2: 2 × **4** = 8, so Q = **4**.

P = 4 and Q = **2** and P = 8 and Q = **1** are also possible pairs of values.

1. **Simplify** the question.

$6 + \triangle + \triangle + \stackrel{\wedge}{\sim} = 17$

$6 + 2\triangle + \stackrel{\wedge}{\sim} = 17$

$2\triangle + \stackrel{\wedge}{\sim} = 11$

So you need values for $\triangle$ and $\stackrel{\wedge}{\sim}$ that give $2\triangle + \stackrel{\wedge}{\sim} = 11$.

Try $\triangle = 1$:

$2\triangle = 2 \times 1 = 2$

$2 + \stackrel{\wedge}{\sim} = 11$, so $\stackrel{\wedge}{\sim} = 9$

Some other pairs of answers are $\triangle = 2$ and $\stackrel{\wedge}{\sim} = 7$ and $\triangle = 4$ and $\stackrel{\wedge}{\sim} = 3$.

Pages 36-37 — Algebra Quiz

Key Words

1. **Sequence**: A list of numbers (or shapes) that follow a pattern. There is a rule that links each number to the one before. Formula: **A rule that connects two or more quantities, so you can work out one quantity when you know the others.** Term: Each number in a number sequence. (1 mark for each)

Now Try These

2. By working out the difference between the terms. (1 mark)

3. The thing you want to work out. (1 mark)

4. Symbols and letters (1 mark for both)

5. False — the difference between the terms is −5. (1 mark)

6. 5 ⑧ 7 ③ (1 mark for both)

7. Divide both sides by 5. (1 mark)

8. 27, 33 and 39 (1 mark for all three correct)

9. Points = 2 × 2 + 1 = 4 + 1 = 5, so she has 5 points. (1 mark)

10. $\bigcirc + 2 \blacksquare = 15$ (1 mark for each correct number)

11. a) Total cost of tickets (in £) = number of friends × 7 (1 mark)

b) Total cost of tickets = 6 × 7 = 42, so it would cost £42. (1 mark)

Measurement

Pages 38-39 — Units

Converting Units

Multiply to go from a big unit to a small unit.

Divide to go from a small unit to a big unit.

1 cm	**10 mm**
1 m	100 cm
1 km	**1000 m**

1 kg	**1000 g**
1 litre	1000 ml

100 cm = 1 m

So divide by **100**:

120 cm ÷ 100 = 1.2 m

1 litre = **1000 ml**

So multiply by **1000**:

0.5 litres × 1000 = 500 ml

Converting Units of Time

1 minute	**60 seconds**
1 hour	**60 minutes**
1 day	**24 hours**
1 week	**7 days**
1 year	**365 days**

There are 366 days in a **leap year**.

1 week = **7 days**

2 weeks = **2 × 7 = 14** days

1 day = **24 hours**

14 days = **14 × 24 = 336 hours**

1 hour = **60 minutes**

4 × 60 = 240 minutes

1 minute = **60 seconds**

240 × 60 = 14 400 seconds

Miles and Kilometres

First divide by **5**:

25 ÷ 5 = 5

Answers

Then multiply by **8**:
5 × 8 = 40 km

≈ means '**approximately equal to**'.

Miles → Kilometres
divide by **5** then multiply by **8**

Kilometres → Miles
divide by **8** then multiply by **5**

First divide by **8**:
96 ÷ 8 = 12
Then multiply by **5**:
12 × 5 = 60 miles

Pages 40-41 — Perimeter, Area and Volume

Area and Perimeter

Area is the space inside a 2D shape.

Perimeter is the distance around the outside of a shape.

Shapes with the same perimeter can have different areas:
Perimeter = **6 + 6 + 6 + 6 = 24** cm
Area = **6 × 6 = 36** cm^2
Perimeter = **2 + 10 + 2 + 10**
    = **24** cm
Area = **10 × 2 = 20** cm^2

Shapes with the same area can have different perimeters:
Perimeter = **3 + 8 + 3 + 8 = 22** cm
Area = **8 × 3 = 24** cm^2
Perimeter = **4 + 6 + 4 + 6 = 20** cm
Area = **6 × 4 = 24** cm^2

Area of Triangles

Area of a triangle
= $\frac{1}{2}$ × **base** × **height**
The base is **20** cm.
The height is **12** cm.

Area = $\frac{1}{2}$ × **20** × **12** = **120** cm^2

Area of Parallelograms

Area of a parallelogram
= base × **height**

Area = base × **height**

Area = **4 × 8 = 32** cm^2
Area of parallelogram
= **9 × 6 = 54** cm^2
Area of coloured triangle
= $\frac{1}{2}$ × **9** × **6** = **27** cm^2
Area of grey part
= **54 − 27 = 27** cm^2

Volume of Cubes and Cuboids

Volume: **the amount of space a 3D shape takes up**.

Volume of a cuboid
= **length × width × height**
Volume = **3 × 6 × 2**
Volume = **36** m^3

Volume is measured in '**cubic**' units:
m^3 → cubic metres
cm^3 → **cubic** centimetres
mm^3 → **cubic millimetres**
km^3 → **cubic kilometres**

Pages 42-43 — Measurement Quiz

Key Words

1. **Area**: The space inside a 2D shape.
    Perimeter: **The distance around the outside of a shape.**
    Volume: The amount of space a 3D shape takes up.
    (1 mark for each)

Now Try These

2. Multiply (1 mark)
3. False (1 mark)
4. Convert the number of days into hours. (1 mark)
5. 60 × 3 = 180 seconds (1 mark)
6. Divide it by 8 then multiply by 5. (1 mark)
7. Area of a triangle
    = $\frac{1}{2}$ × **base** × **height**
    (1 mark for each)

8. a) 1 km = **1000** m
    b) 2 cm = **20** mm
    c) 500g = **0.5** kg
    (1 mark for each)

9. Area of a parallelogram
    = base × height
    Area = **7 × 5 = 35** cm^2
    (1 mark)

10. Volume of a cuboid
    = length × width × height
    (1 mark)

Geometry

Pages 44-45 — 2D Shapes

Quadrilaterals

A quadrilateral is a shape with **4** sides.

4 equal sides
4 equal angles of **90°**
2 pairs of parallel sides

2 pairs of equal sides
4 equal angles of **90°**
2 pairs of **parallel** sides
2 lines of symmetry

4 equal sides
2 pairs of equal angles
2 pairs of parallel sides
2 lines of **symmetry**

1 pair of equal **angles**
No parallel sides
1 line of **symmetry**

2 pairs of equal sides
2 pairs of equal **angles**
2 pairs of **parallel** sides
No lines of symmetry

1 pair of **parallel** sides

Most trapeziums have **no** lines of symmetry, but ones like this have exactly **one**:

Other Polygons

3 equal sides
3 equal angles of **60°**
3 lines of symmetry

Answers

2 equal sides
2 equal angles
No **parallel** sides
1 line of symmetry

Regular polygon: a shape with all equal **sides** and equal **angles**.

Irregular polygon: a shape that doesn't have all equal **sides** and **equal angles**.

Circles

Radius: distance from the **edge** to the centre

diameter: distance across the circle through the **centre**

circumference: the outside edge of a circle

The diameter is **twice** the radius.

Diameter = 2 × radius
Radius = diameter ÷ **2**
Radius = **14** ÷ 2 = **7 cm**

Drawing Polygons

Measure and draw sides with a **ruler**.

Measure and draw angles with a **protractor**.

Equilateral triangles have **three** equal sides and three **60°** angles.

Pages 46-47 — Angles

Angle Rules

Angles on a straight line add up to **180°**.

a + b + c = **180°**

Angles on a straight line add up to **180°**.
So 56° + 71° + p = **180°**
p = **180°** − 56° − 71° = **53°**

Angles around a point add up to **360°**.

w + x + y + z = **360°**

Angles around a point add up to **360°**.
So 128° + 64° + **90°** + q = 360°
q = **360°** − 128° − 64° − **90°** = **78°**

Vertically opposite angles are **equal**.

a = **c** and b = **d**

r and the 54° angle are **vertically opposite**, so they are **equal**.
So r = **54°**.

Angles in a Triangle

Angles in a triangle add up to **180°**.

The triangle is isosceles, so this angle is **67°**.
Angles in a triangle add up to **180°**,
so x + 67° + **67°** = **180°**.
x = **180°** − **67°** − **67°** = **46°**

Angles in a Quadrilateral

Angles in a quadrilateral add up to **360°**.

Angles in a quadrilateral add up to **360°**, so
s + 54° + 57° + 108° = **360°**
s = **360°** − 54° − 57° − 108° = **141°**

Angles in Polygons

Exterior angles

Interior angles

For all polygons:
Interior angle = **180°** − exterior angle
Sum of exterior angles = **360°**
Sum of interior angles
= (n − **2**) × **180°**

For regular polygons ONLY:
All interior angles are **equal**.
All exterior angles are **equal**.

Exterior angle = $\dfrac{360°}{n}$

A hexagon has **6** sides, so n = **6**.

Exterior angle = $\dfrac{360°}{n}$ = $\dfrac{360°}{6}$
= **60°**

Interior angle = **180°** − **60°** = **120°**

Pages 48-49 — 3D Shapes

Nets and 3D Shapes

A net is a **2D** shape that can be folded to make a **3D** shape.

Each shape in the net is a **face** of the 3D shape.

Cube: 6 **square** faces
6 **squares**

Cuboid: **6** rectangular faces
6 rectangles

Square-based pyramid:
4 triangular faces
1 **square** face
4 triangles
1 **square**

Triangular prism:
2 **triangular** faces
3 rectangular faces
2 **triangles**
3 rectangles

Tetrahedron
(**triangle**-based pyramid):
4 triangular faces
4 triangles

More About Nets

A 3D shape can have **more** than one net.

E.g.

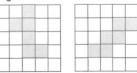

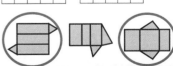

The **triangular** faces would touch, so it **won't** make a triangular prism.

Answers

Drawing 3D Shapes

This face is **3** cm × **2** cm
This face is **3** cm × **1** cm

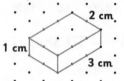

Pages 50-51 — Coordinates & Transformations

Coordinates

Each quarter of the grid is called a **quadrant**.

number on the **horizontal** axis
→(x, y)←
number on the **vertical** axis

If x is positive, the point is **right** of the origin.
If x is negative, the point is **left** of the origin.
If y is positive, the point is **above** the origin.
If y is negative, the point is **below** the origin.

A has coordinates (**–3**, **1**).
B has coordinates (**1**, **–2**).
The origin has coordinates (**0**, **0**).

Translations

Translating by a positive number moves shapes right or **up**.

Translating by a negative number moves shapes **left** or down.

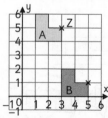

Translate the shape 2 units to the **right** and 4 units **down**.

The coordinates of the translated vertex Z are (**5**, **1**).

Missing Coordinates

A is directly **below** B, so they have the **same** x-coordinate. So the x-coordinate of A is **–1**.

The **difference** between the x-coordinates of B and C is **4**, so each side of the square is **4** units. A is **4** units below B, so the y-coordinate of A is **3 – 4 = –1**. So A has coordinates (**–1, –1**).

Reflections

Reflect shapes in a **mirror line**. Each point and its reflection are the **same** distance from the **mirror line**.

Count the number of units to the **mirror line**.
Count the same number on the other side of the **mirror line**.
Draw the **reflected** point.

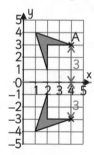

Vertex A is 3 units **above** the x-axis, so the reflected vertex A is 3 units **below** the x-axis.

Pages 52-53 — Geometry Quiz

Key Words

1. Quadrilateral: **A shape with 4 sides.**
   Irregular polygon: **A shape that doesn't have all equal sides and equal angles.**

Translation: When a shape slides from one place to another on a grid.
Net: A 2D shape that can be folded to make a 3D shape.
(1 mark for each)

Key Diagrams

2.

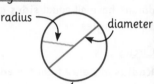

(1 mark for each correct label)

Now Try These

3. a) trapezium (1 mark)
   b) one (1 mark)

4. c = 40° (1 mark)
   d = 140° (1 mark)

5. 360° (1 mark)

6. A (1 mark)

7.

Shape	Pairs of equal angles	Pairs of parallel sides	Lines of symmetry
Rhombus	2	**2**	**2**
Kite	**1**	**0**	1
Parallelogram	**2**	2	**0**

(1 mark for each correct row)

8. Divide 360° by the number of sides (n). (1 mark)

Statistics

Pages 54-55 — Pie Charts

Pie Chart Basics

Pie charts: show things as **proportions**. A slice of a pie chart is called a **sector**. A bigger **sector** means a bigger **proportion**.